House Plans One Story

Unveiling the Beauty of Single-Story Living with these Eye-Catching House Plans with Home Office and Bedrooms

Mary O. White

Contents

Introduction

Welcome to "One Story Wonders: Unveiling the Beauty of Single-Story Living." In the pages that follow, we invite you to embark on a captivating journey through the world of one-story house plans, where simplicity and elegance harmoniously blend to create homes that are both beautiful and highly functional.

Our Styles page, featuring dozens of styles, serves as the perfect starting point for your home plan search. We understand that choosing the perfect house plan can be a daunting task. That's why we've made it easier for you. Simply select the style or styles you prefer, and our site will filter and display only those plans that match your chosen style. From there, you can further refine your search by various requirements, compare plans, save favorites, and create detailed searches tailored to your needs.

Within the pages of this book, you'll discover a treasure trove of architectural marvels meticulously designed to embrace the tranquility and convenience that single-level living offers. Whether you're a first-time homeowner, a growing family in need of more space, or an empty-nester looking to downsize without sacrificing style, this book is your gateway to a realm where dreams become reality.

At its core, this collection celebrates the timeless allure of one-story living. It showcases a range of house plans thoughtfully curated to suit diverse lifestyles and tastes. From cozy cottages exuding warmth and intimacy to sprawling ranch-style estates embodying grandeur, each design captures the essence of comfort and convenience.

However, this book is more than just a compilation of floor plans and architectural renderings. It is an exploration of the unique advantages that one-story living presents. We delve into the seamless flow between rooms, the effortless accessibility that eliminates stairs and barriers, and the inherent connection to nature as each space seamlessly opens up to the surrounding environment.

Through vivid descriptions, stunning visuals, and expert insights, "One Story Wonders" aims to inspire you, igniting your imagination and paving the way for your personal journey into the world of single-story living. Whether you're an aspiring homeowner, an architect, or simply someone with a passion for the art of construction, this book is designed to be your trusted companion and an endless source of inspiration.

So, join us as we embark on a captivating exploration of one-story house plans. Uncover the architectural gems that await, and let the enchantment of single-story living unfold before your eyes. With "One Story Wonders," your dream home is just a page away.

Start your home search from our house plan Styles page and discover the house plan of your dreams. Let the adventure begin!

Rustic Haven: A One-Story Family House Plan with Stunning Exterior

Step into the world of rustic elegance with our one-story family house plan, where timeless charm and modern comfort seamlessly merge. This thoughtfully designed home offers less than 3,000 square feet of heated living space, featuring 4 bedrooms and 3.5 baths. With a 3-car courtyard garage that includes a dedicated shop, mechanical space, and even a dog wash, this plan caters to every aspect of family life.

As you enter the home through the mudroom from the garage or the inviting French doors from the grand porch with its two-story roof, you'll immediately feel the warmth and welcome of the foyer. The central living core is an open expanse, bathed in natural light. The soaring 19-foot, two-story ceiling creates an airy and bright atmosphere, encompassing the great room, dining room, and kitchen.

To the left of this central space, you'll discover a powder room, followed by the laundry room and the primary bedroom suite. The suite has been meticulously designed with privacy and luxury in mind. It offers private access to covered outdoor living areas, a beautifully appointed bathroom, and a generous walk-in closet with convenient pass-through access to the laundry room.

As you head in the opposite direction from the entry, you'll find yourself in a spacious vaulted flex room. The possibilities for this room are endless—it could serve as an office, a home gym, an art studio, a music room, a game room, a theatre, or any other space that suits your family's unique needs and interests. Completing the home are three additional bedrooms, one with an ensuite bathroom and walk-in closet, and the other two sharing a full bath just outside. The floor plan of this remarkable house offers both functionality and style, with a total heated area of 2,896 square feet. Our attention to detail extends to the foundation options, including standard choices such as crawl, and optional foundations like walkout, slab, and basement to suit your preferences. The exterior walls are constructed with 2x6 materials, ensuring durability and energy efficiency. Dimensions-wise, this house spans a width of 100 feet and a depth of 78 feet 6 inches. The 3-car garage provides ample space for vehicles and storage. We invite you to explore the beauty and functionality of this one-story family house plan. Its rustic charm, stunning exterior, and well-designed layout make it an ideal haven for your family's dreams to unfold. With 4 bedrooms, 3.5 baths, and a range of flexible spaces, this home is ready to embrace your unique lifestyle.

Floor Plan: *Main Level*

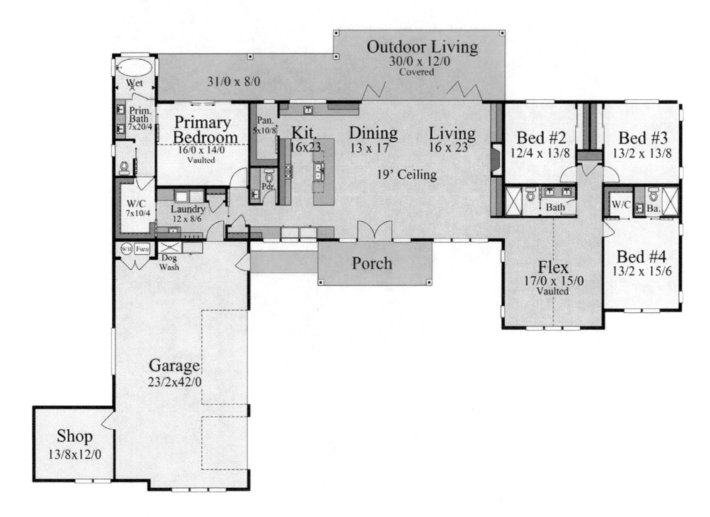

Plan details

Square Footage Breakdown
Total Heated Area:2,896 sq. ft.
1st Floor:2,896 sq. ft.
Beds/Baths
Bedrooms:4
Full Bathrooms:3
Half Bathrooms:1
Foundation Type
Standard Foundations: Crawl
Optional Foundations: Walkout, Slab, Basement
Exterior Walls
Standard Type(s):2x6
Dimensions

Width:100' 0"		
Depth:78' 6"		
	Garage	
Count:3 cars		

Expansive Elegance: A One-Story House Plan with a Stunning Foyer

Welcome to the epitome of luxury and versatility—a one-story house plan that can be expanded to accommodate up to five bedrooms with the optional finished lower level. From the moment you step inside the dramatic foyer, you'll be captivated by the grandeur and thoughtful design of this remarkable home.

The highlight of this house plan is the curved stair in the foyer, creating a striking focal point and a beautiful welcome. This architectural feature not only adds elegance but also offers access to the lower level, where the possibilities for additional living space are endless.

As you move from the foyer, you'll enter the inviting great room, which seamlessly flows into the nook and kitchen area. French doors beckon you to a large sun deck at the back of the house, providing a perfect setting to soak in the views and savor outdoor living. Another set of French doors opens to a screened covered deck, offering a serene space to relax and enjoy the surrounding environment.

The master suite is designed with comfort and luxury in mind. It boasts a spacious sitting area that provides a private retreat within your own home. The suite also features a large segmented walk-in closet, ensuring ample storage space for your wardrobe and personal belongings.

Additionally, off the foyer, you'll discover a home office that offers panoramic views over the front porch. This space combines functionality with charm, providing an inspiring environment for work or study.

This one-story house plan marries elegance with practicality, offering a versatile layout that can be expanded to suit your needs. With the option to add up to five bedrooms, including two on the main floor and three below, this home provides ample space for a growing family, accommodating guests, or creating additional recreational areas.

The attention to detail and thoughtful design extend throughout this exceptional house plan, creating a harmonious blend of style and functionality. From the dramatic foyer to the well-appointed living spaces, this home is a testament to luxurious living. Experience the splendor of this expandable one-story house plan with its dramatic foyer. With the option to customize and expand the living space, this home offers flexibility and elegance, catering to your unique lifestyle. Embrace the possibilities and envision a future filled with comfort, style, and endless opportunities for cherished memories.

FRONT ELEVATION

LEFT ELEVATION

REAR ELEVATION

RIGHT ELEVATION

Floor Plan

Main Level

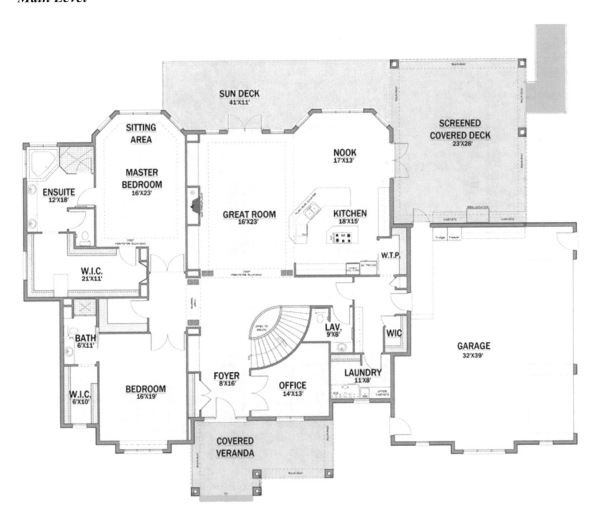

SUN DECK
41'X11'

SITTING
AREA

MASTER
BEDROOM
16'X23'

NOOK
17'X13'

SCREENED
COVERED DECK
23'X28'

ENSUITE
12'X18'

GREAT ROOM
16'X23'

KITCHEN
18'X15'

W.T.P.

W.I.C.
21'X11'

BATH
6'X11'

LAV.
9'X8'

WIC

GARAGE
32'X39'

W.I.C.
6'X10'

BEDROOM
16'X19'

FOYER
8'X16'

OFFICE
14'X13'

LAUNDRY
11'X8'

COVERED
VERANDA

Basement

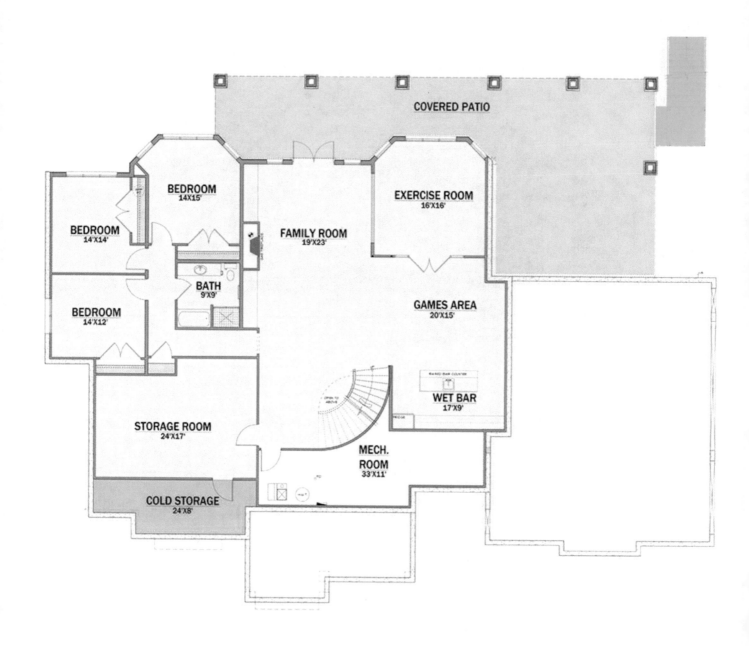

Plan details

Square Footage Breakdown
Total Heated Area:3,396 sq. ft.
1st Floor:3,396 sq. ft.
Deck:739 sq. ft.
Screened Porch:644 sq. ft.
Optional Lower Level:2,310 sq. ft.

Beds/Baths
Bedrooms:2, 3, 4, or 5
Full Bathrooms:2 or 3
Half Bathrooms:1

Foundation Type
Standard Foundations: Walkout

Exterior Walls
Standard Type(s):2x6

Dimensions
Width:99' 0"
Depth:60' 0"
Max Ridge Height:28' 0"

Garage
Type: Attached
Area:1225 sq. ft.
Count:3 cars
Entry Location: Side

Ceiling Heights
Floor / Height: First Floor / 12' 0"

Roof Details
Primary Pitch:6 on 12
Secondary Pitch:8 on 12
Framing Type: Truss

Transitional Bliss: A Spacious One-Story Home Plan with a Striking Flex Room

Step into a world of contemporary elegance with our one-story Transitional home plan, designed to offer comfort, style, and versatility. With 4 bedrooms, 2.5 baths, and a total living space of 2,324 square feet, this home is a testament to thoughtful design and modern living.

As you approach the house, you'll be greeted by an inviting arched front porch, setting the stage for the beauty that awaits inside. The open and spacious living area boasts a soaring 12-foot ceiling, creating an atmosphere of grandeur and openness. Seamlessly blending the family room, dining area, and kitchen, this area facilitates easy interaction and a sense of togetherness for your family and guests.

The kitchen is a chef's dream, with U-shaped cabinetry surrounding a prep island at its center. A convenient walk-in pantry is located nearby, ensuring ample storage space for all your culinary needs. Sliding glass doors beckon you to the back porch, where you can relax and entertain. There's plenty of room for a grill and a dining table, allowing you to make the most of outdoor living.

Tucked behind the double garage, you'll find the tranquil primary bedroom. This private retreat features a luxurious 5-fixture bathroom and pocket-door access to the adjacent laundry room, adding convenience to your daily routines.

The right side of the home is adorned with two secondary bedrooms, perfect for family members or guests. Additionally, there's a flexible third room that can be adapted to suit your needs—whether it be an office, an additional bedroom, or a study area.

This one-story Transitional home plan seamlessly combines functionality with modern design elements. It offers a perfect balance of comfort and style, catering to the needs and aspirations of a contemporary lifestyle.

Embrace the charm and versatility of this one-story Transitional home plan, where comfort and elegance harmoniously coexist. With spacious living areas, a well-appointed kitchen, and multiple bedrooms, this home provides an ideal setting for creating cherished memories. Whether you desire a peaceful retreat or a space for entertaining, this plan offers the perfect canvas to bring your vision to life.

FRONT ELEVATION

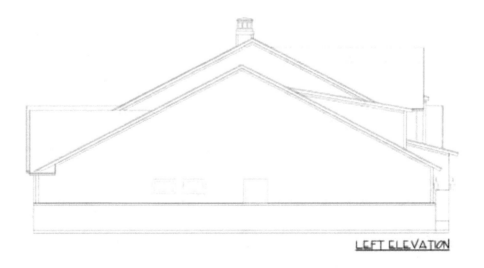

LEFT ELEVATION

17

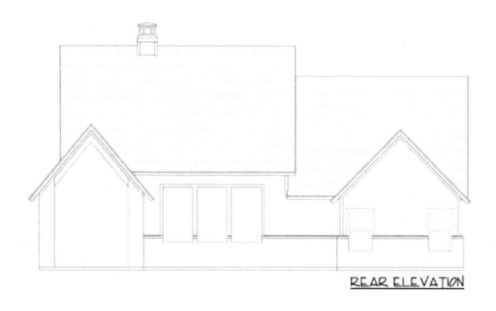

REAR ELEVATION

RIGHT ELEVATION

Floor Plan

Main Level

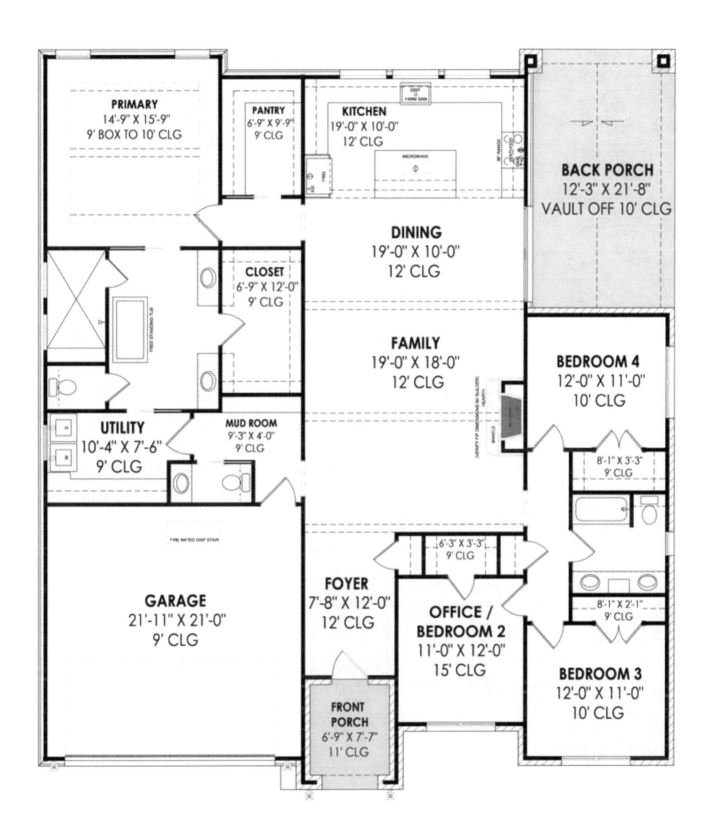

PRIMARY
14'-9" X 15'-9"
9' BOX TO 10' CLG

PANTRY
6'-9" X 9'-9"
9' CLG

KITCHEN
19'-0" X 10'-0"
12' CLG

MICROWAVE

BACK PORCH
12'-3" X 21'-8"
VAULT OFF 10' CLG

DINING
19'-0" X 10'-0"
12' CLG

CLOSET
6'-9" X 12'-0"
9' CLG

FAMILY
19'-0" X 18'-0"
12' CLG

BEDROOM 4
12'-0" X 11'-0"
10' CLG

8'-1" X 3'-3"
9' CLG

UTILITY
10'-4" X 7'-6"
9' CLG

MUD ROOM
9'-3" X 4'-0"
9' CLG

FIRE RATED DISP STAIR

6'-3" X 3'-3"
9' CLG

8'-1" X 2'-1"
9' CLG

GARAGE
21'-11" X 21'-0"
9' CLG

FOYER
7'-8" X 12'-0"
12' CLG

OFFICE /
BEDROOM 2
11'-0" X 12'-0"
15' CLG

BEDROOM 3
12'-0" X 11'-0"
10' CLG

FRONT
PORCH
6'-9" X 7'-7"
11' CLG

Plan details

Square Footage Breakdown
Total Heated Area:2,324 sq. ft.
1st Floor:2,324 sq. ft.
Porch, Combined:339 sq. ft.
Porch, Rear:268 sq. ft.
Porch, Front:71 sq. ft.
Brick Pocket:102 sq. ft.
Beds/Baths
Bedrooms:3 or 4
Full Bathrooms:2
Half Bathrooms:1
Foundation Type
Standard Foundations: Monolithic Slab
Exterior Walls
Standard Type(s):2x4
Optional Type(s):2x6
Dimensions
Width:55' 0"
Depth:62' 0"
Max Ridge Height:31' 0"
Garage
Type: Attached
Area:484 sq. ft.
Count:2 cars
Entry Location: Front
Ceiling Heights
Floor / Height: First Floor / 9' 0"
Roof Details
Primary Pitch:6 on 12
Secondary Pitch:14 on 12
Framing Type: Stick

Contemporary Elegance: A Captivating One-Story Modern Prairie-Style House Plan

Discover the epitome of modern living with our stunning one-story Modern Prairie-style house plan. This home exudes curb appeal and is an ideal choice for those seeking a starter home or builders looking to create a spec home. With its low roofline, not only does it add to the contemporary allure, but it also helps reduce roofing costs—a true win-win! The modern windows and bold columns flanking the entryway complete the picture of sophistication.

As you step inside, you'll be welcomed into a foyer with an impressive 11-foot ceiling, setting the tone for the grandeur that awaits. The foyer seamlessly leads you into the spacious great room, where an elegant boxed ceiling and a cozy fireplace create a warm and inviting atmosphere.

The great room opens up to the kitchen, with a raised eat-at bar serving as a delightful connection point. The kitchen boasts ample counter space and cupboards, providing abundant storage for all your culinary needs. Adjacent to the kitchen, an attached breakfast room offers a perfect spot for casual meals and cherished moments with loved ones around the table.

On the left side of the home, you'll find bedrooms 2 and 3, each offering their own generous closets. These bedrooms share a full bath with two sinks conveniently placed in between. From this hallway, you can access the 2-car courtyard entry garage and the laundry room. Adjacent to the garage entry, a charming "kid's nook" awaits, featuring a bench and coat hooks—a perfect little mudroom or drop zone as you arrive home.

From the hallway or the great room, you can enter bedroom 4, which can easily transform into a versatile space to suit your individual needs—a media room, a guest room, or a home office, the possibilities are endless.

The right side of the home is dedicated entirely to the luxurious master suite. The master bedroom boasts an elegant 10-foot boxed ceiling and provides direct access to the grilling porch—an outdoor oasis just a step away. The master bath is a haven of relaxation, featuring a glass shower, a freestanding tub, a dual sink vanity, a private toilet room, and a spacious walk-in closet.

Indulge in the contemporary elegance of this one-story Modern Prairie-style house plan. With its captivating design, spacious living areas, and luxurious master suite, this home offers both style and functionality. From the inviting great room to the well-appointed kitchen and the versatile bedrooms, every detail has been thoughtfully crafted to ensure comfort and sophistication.

Floor Plan

Main Level

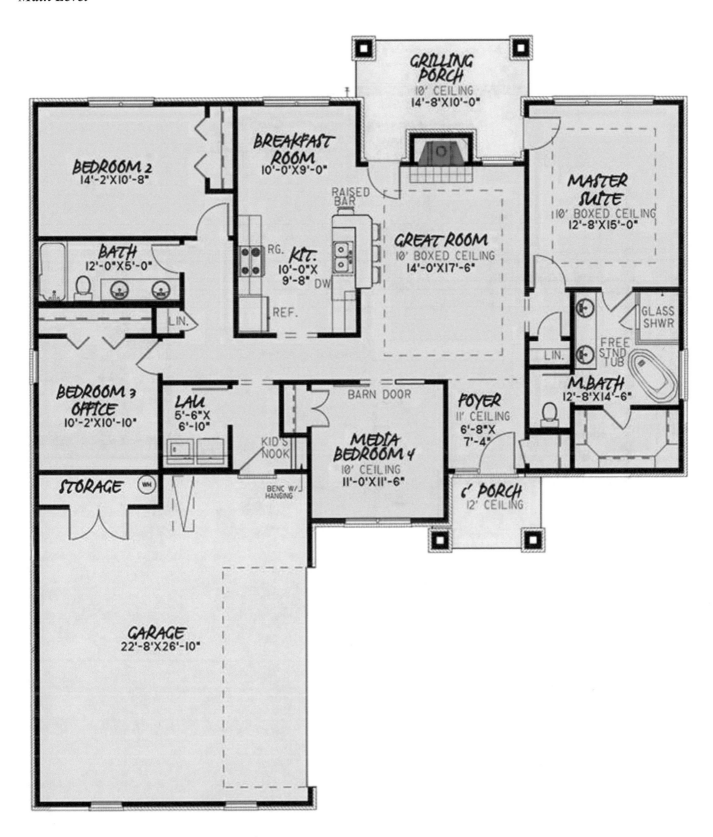

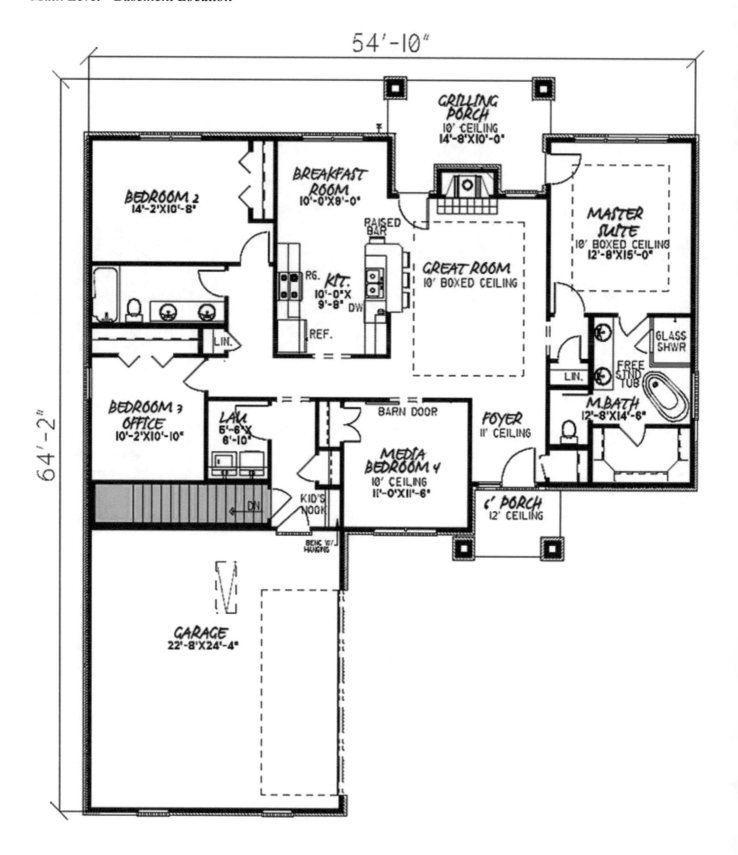

Plan details

Square Footage Breakdown
Total Heated Area:1,649 sq. ft.
1st Floor:1,649 sq. ft.
Porch, Combined:188 sq. ft.
Beds/Baths
Bedrooms:2, 3, or 4
Full Bathrooms:2
Foundation Type
Standard Foundations: Slab, Crawl
Optional Foundations: Daylight, Basement
Exterior Walls
Standard Type(s):2x4
Optional Type(s):2x6
Dimensions
Width:54' 10"
Depth:62' 8"
Max Ridge Height:17' 9"
Garage
Type: Attached
Area:632 sq. ft.
Count:2 cars
Entry Location:Courtyard

Contemporary Charm: A Stylish One-Story Split Bedroom Transitional Tudor Home Plan

Experience the perfect blend of timeless elegance and contemporary design with our one-story split bedroom Transitional Tudor-style house plan. Boasting a painted brick exterior adorned with wood brackets and accents, this home exudes a modern aesthetic that is sure to captivate. Step inside and discover a thoughtfully designed floor plan that seamlessly combines the family room, kitchen, and dining room into a single, inviting space for entertaining.

As you enter through the covered entry, you'll be greeted by an elongated foyer with impressive 12-foot ceilings. This grand entrance leads you to an open floor plan that effortlessly merges the family room, kitchen, and dining room, creating a harmonious environment for social gatherings.

The family room is adorned with decorative beams and features a cozy fireplace on the side wall, making it a space you'll want to relax in and enjoy. Abundant windows line the back wall, providing ample natural light, and a door leads you to a large covered and vaulted back porch—a perfect sanctuary for outdoor relaxation.

The kitchen is a chef's delight, with an island housing a sink and dishwasher on one side and seating on the other, allowing for both functionality and social interaction. A walk-in pantry, conveniently located steps away from the garage entry and the kitchen itself, offers ample storage space for your culinary essentials.

The master suite is a tranquil retreat, offering direct laundry access through the spacious walk-in closet. A five-fixture bath, complete with a compartmented toilet and two vanities, adds a touch of luxury and convenience to the suite.

On the opposite side of the home, three bedrooms share a well-appointed bathroom with two vanities. By sealing off the door to Bedroom 4 and opening it to the foyer, you can transform this space into a home office—an ideal setting for productivity and focus.

Indulge in the contemporary charm of this one-story split bedroom Transitional Tudor-style home plan. With its painted brick exterior, stylish accents, and thoughtfully designed interior, this home offers both timeless elegance and modern functionality. From the inviting open floor plan to the cozy family room and well-equipped kitchen, every detail has been carefully crafted to create a space that is both aesthetically pleasing and practical for everyday living.

FRONT ELEVATION

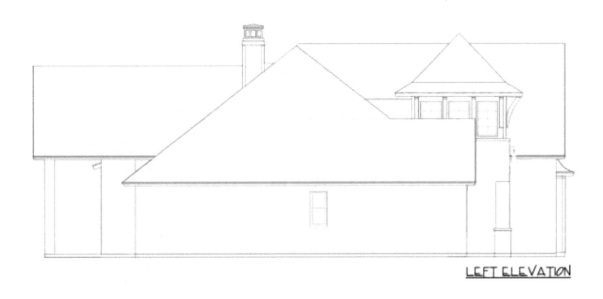

LEFT ELEVATION

31

REAR ELEVATION

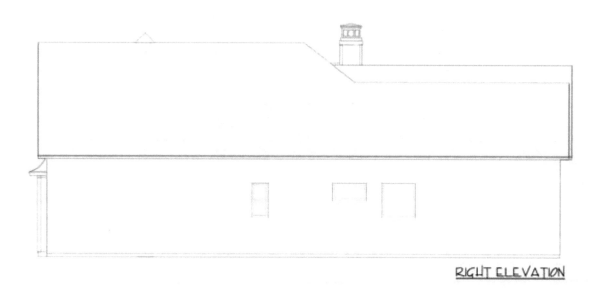

RIGHT ELEVATION

Floor Plan

Main Level

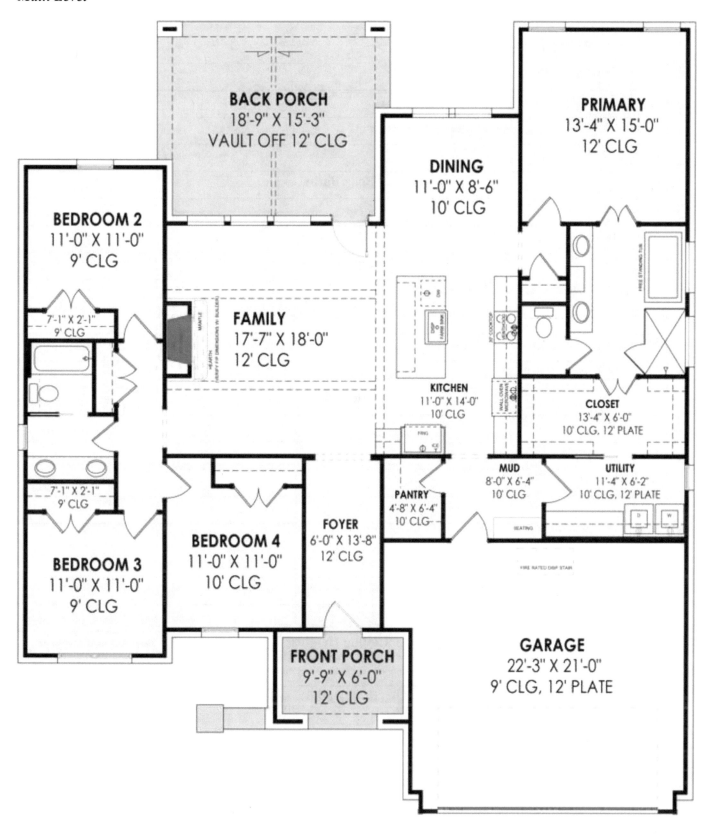

Plan details

Square Footage Breakdown
Total Heated Area:1,952 sq. ft.
1st Floor:1,952 sq. ft.
Porch, Combined:361 sq. ft.
Porch, Rear:272 sq. ft.
Porch, Front:89 sq. ft.
Brick Pocket:102 sq. ft.
Beds/Baths
Bedrooms:4
Full Bathrooms:2
Foundation Type
Standard Foundations: Monolithic Slab
Exterior Walls
Standard Type(s):2x4
Optional Type(s):2x6
Dimensions
Width:55' 0"
Depth:62' 3"
Max Ridge Height:25' 8"
Garage
Type: Attached
Area:499 sq. ft.
Count:2 cars
Entry Location: Front
Ceiling Heights
Floor / Height: First Floor / 9' 0"
Roof Details
Primary Pitch:9 on 12
Secondary Pitch:12 on 12
Framing Type: Stick

Single-Story Comfort: A 4-Bedroom Texas-Style Ranch Home Plan

Experience the ease of single-story living with our 4-bedroom Texas (Hill Country)-style ranch home plan. Boasting a charming mix of stone and stucco on the exterior, this home exudes a rustic elegance. The oversized windows flanking the entryway create an impressive statement, welcoming you with abundant natural light.

Step inside and discover an office tucked behind French doors in the foyer, offering a private space for productivity and focus. Continuing forward, an open floor plan awaits, featuring a vaulted great room with a wood-burning fireplace—a warm and inviting centerpiece for gatherings and relaxation.

The kitchen is a chef's dream, complete with a large island featuring twin sinks and ample space for casual seating. A conveniently located pantry, just steps away from the family entrance, makes unloading groceries a breeze, adding to the practicality of the design. For those who enjoy dining al fresco, a rear porch off the dining room provides a delightful option for outdoor meals and entertaining.

On the right side of the home, three bedrooms are clustered together, offering comfort and privacy. Additionally, a game room situated at the back of the home provides the perfect space for children to burn off their extra energy and indulge in playful activities.

35

The master suite is thoughtfully positioned in the back-left corner of the home, ensuring privacy and tranquility. Featuring a 10-foot tray ceiling, the master bedroom exudes an air of sophistication. Dual vanities, a large walk-in closet, a tub, a shower, and access to the laundry room through a pocket door showcase a smart and efficient design, catering to both practicality and luxury.

Embrace the comfort and charm of single-story living with this 4-bedroom Texas-style ranch home plan. From the captivating exterior to the open and inviting interior spaces, this home offers a perfect blend of style and functionality. Whether it's the vaulted great room, the well-appointed kitchen, or the private master suite, every detail has been carefully considered to create a space that is both aesthetically pleasing and conducive to modern living.

FRONT ELEVATION

42

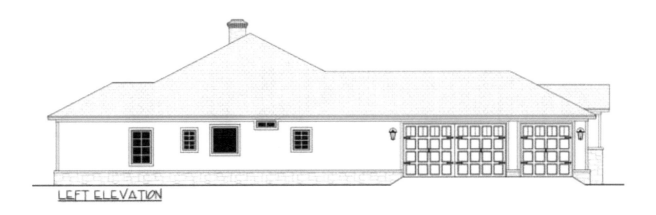

LEFT ELEVATION

REAR ELEVATION

43

Floor Plan

Main Level

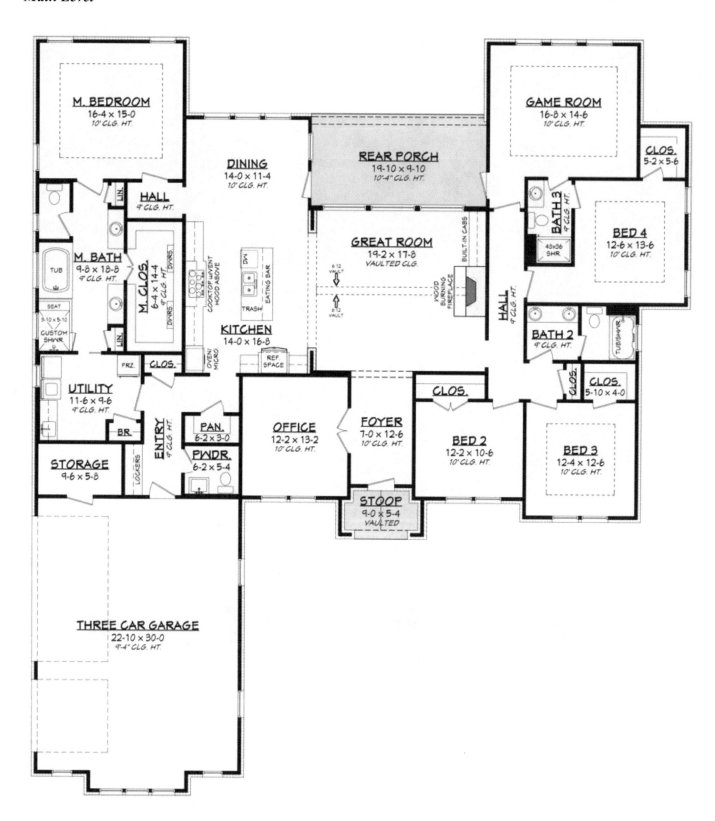

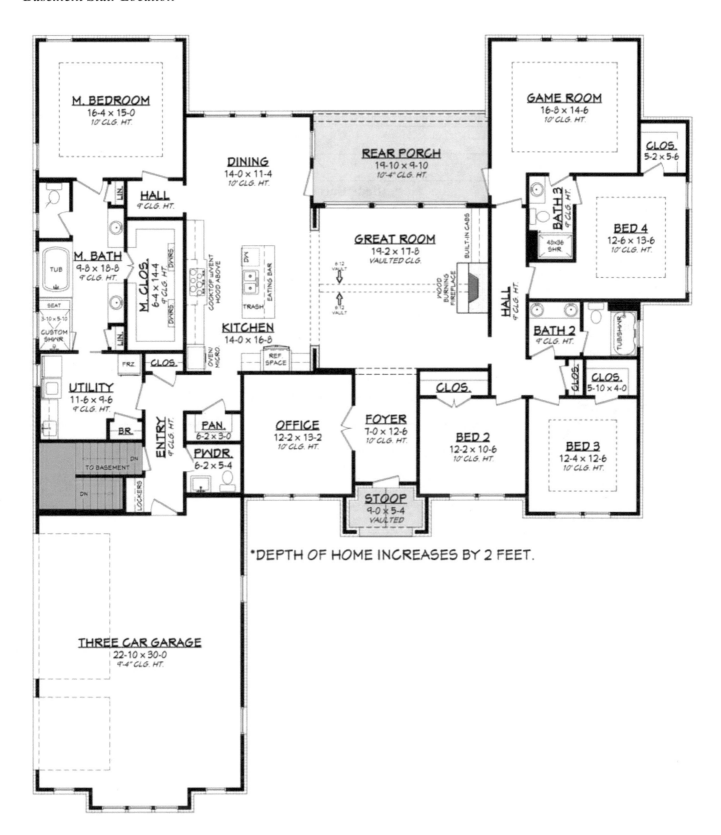

M. BEDROOM
16-4 x 15-0
10' CLG. HT.

GAME ROOM
16-8 x 14-6
10' CLG. HT.

DINING
14-0 x 11-4
10' CLG. HT.

REAR PORCH
19-10 x 9-10
10'-4" CLG. HT.

CLOS.
5-2 x 5-6

HALL
9' CLG. HT.

BATH 3
9' CLG. HT.

BED 4
12-6 x 13-6
10' CLG. HT.

LIN.

M. BATH
9-8 x 18-8
9' CLG. HT.

TUB

SEAT

3-10 x 5-10

CUSTOM SHWR.

M. CLOS.
6-4 x 14-4
9' CLG. HT.

GREAT ROOM
19-2 x 17-8
VAULTED CLG.

WOOD BURNING FIREPLACE

BUILT-IN CABS

HALL
9' CLG. HT.

BATH 2
9' CLG. HT.

TUB/SHWR

COOKTOP w/VENT HOOD ABOVE

KITCHEN
14-0 x 16-8

TRASH

EATING BAR

OVEN

MICRO.

FRZ.

CLOS.

REF. SPACE

CLOS.

CLOS.

CLOS.
5-10 x 4-0

UTILITY
11-6 x 9-6
9' CLG. HT.

BR.

ENTRY
9' CLG. HT.

PAN.
6-2 x 3-0

PWDR.
6-2 x 5-4

OFFICE
12-2 x 13-2
10' CLG. HT.

FOYER
7-0 x 12-6
10' CLG. HT.

CLOS.

BED 2
12-2 x 10-6
10' CLG. HT.

BED 3
12-4 x 12-6
10' CLG. HT.

TO BASEMENT

DN

DN

LOCKERS

STOOP
9-0 x 5-4
VAULTED

*DEPTH OF HOME INCREASES BY 2 FEET.

THREE CAR GARAGE
22-10 x 30-0
9'-4" CLG. HT.

Plan details

Square Footage Breakdown
Total Heated Area:3,044 sq. ft.
1st Floor:3,044 sq. ft.
Porch, Combined:246 sq. ft.
Porch, Rear:198 sq. ft.
Porch, Front:48 sq. ft.
Beds/Baths
Bedrooms:4
Full Bathrooms:3
Half Bathrooms:1
Foundation Type
Standard Foundations: Slab, Crawl
Optional Foundations: Basement, Walkout
Exterior Walls
Standard Type(s):2x4
Optional Type(s):2x6
Dimensions
Width:74' 0"
Depth:82' 10"
Max Ridge Height:23' 0"
Garage
Type: Attached
Area:736 sq. ft.
Count:3 cars
Entry Location: Side
Ceiling Heights
Floor / Height: Lower Level / 9' 4"First Floor / 9' 0"
Roof Details
Primary Pitch:6 on 12
Framing Type: Stick

Craftsman Charm: A Spacious One-Story House Plan with Split Bedrooms

Discover the allure of Craftsman-style living with our one-story house plan, offering a perfect balance of functionality and elegance. This thoughtfully designed home features a private master bedroom, a delightful screened porch, and an oversized 4-car garage—a haven for both relaxation and practicality.

As you step inside, you'll be greeted by a large and open great room straight ahead, serving as the heart of the home. A four-paneled glass door leads to the rear screened porch, seamlessly connecting indoor and outdoor living spaces. Three columns elegantly define the area, adding a touch of architectural sophistication.

The adjoining kitchen effortlessly connects to the dining room, creating a harmonious flow and allowing for easy conversation when entertaining guests. The kitchen boasts a prep island, providing ample workspace for culinary endeavors, while a walk-in pantry, conveniently located nearby, ensures that essentials are always within reach.

The master bedroom occupies the left side of the design, offering a private retreat. It features a spacious walk-in closet with direct access to the laundry room—a practical and time-saving feature. On the opposite side of the home, Bedrooms 2 and 3 are situated, providing comfortable and separate spaces for family members or guests. These bedrooms share a compartmentalized bath, complete with two vanities for added convenience.

The 4-car garage is a standout feature, offering ample space for vehicles and additional storage needs. Its extra-long design provides room for organizing belongings, while a rear-facing overhead door allows easy access for lawn equipment. Inside the garage, a powder bath within the mudroom ensures a convenient and efficient exit in the morning rush. Indulge in the timeless charm of this one-story Craftsman-style house plan, where comfort and style seamlessly blend. From the inviting great room and well-appointed kitchen to the private master suite and split bedrooms, every aspect of this home has been meticulously crafted to create a space that is both aesthetically pleasing and practical for modern living.

FRONT ELEVATION

Floor Plan

Main Level

MASTER
BEDROOM
15'-0" x 14'-0"
10' CLG.
9' CLG.

9' CLG.
9' CLG.

MASTER
BATH

GARAGE
24'-11" x 38'-0"

W.I.C.
6'-8" x 12'-2"
9' CLG.

PANTRY
8'-0" x 5'-0"

LAUNDRY
7'-10" x 6'-8"
9' CLG.

DINING
ROOM
14'-4" x 13'-4"
9' CLG.

KITCHEN
14'-4" x 15'-0"
9' CLG.

MUD ROOM
14'-8" x 7'-8"
9' CLG.

BATH
9' CLG.

SCREEN
PORCH
19'-4" x 12'-4"

GREAT
ROOM
18'-1" x 17'-0"
12' CLG.

DROPPED HEADER

DROPPED HEADER

FOYER
7'-9" x 8'-4"
9' CLG.

DOWN

PORCH

BEDROOM #3
12'-0" x 12'-0"
9' CLG.

W.I.C.
7'-8" x 5'-0"
9' CLG.

BATH
9' CLG.

BEDROOM #2
12'-0" x 12'-0"
9' CLG.

GARAGE
29'-8" x 28'-6"

Plan details

Square Footage Breakdown
Total Heated Area:2,321 sq. ft.
1st Floor:2,321 sq. ft.
Porch, Combined:232 sq. ft.
Basement Unfinished:2,192 sq. ft.
Beds/Baths
Bedrooms:3
Full Bathrooms:2
Half Bathrooms:1
Foundation Type
Standard Foundations: Basement, Daylight, Walkout
Optional Foundations: Slab, Crawl
Exterior Walls
Standard Type(s):2x6
Dimensions
Width:87' 0"
Depth:72' 4"
Max Ridge Height:28' 9"
Garage
Type: Attached
Area:1852 sq. ft.
Count:3 cars
Entry Location: Side, Front
Ceiling Heights
Floor / Height: First Floor / 9' 0"
Roof Details
Primary Pitch:10 on 12
Secondary Pitch:9 on 12
Framing Type: Truss

Elegant Simplicity: A One-Story House Plan with an Ideal Floor Plan

Experience the beauty of Southern elegance with this one-level home plan, featuring a steep hip roof that adds a touch of charm. Despite its modest size, this home offers the convenience of four bedrooms arranged in a split bedroom layout—a perfect combination of functionality and comfort.

Step inside and discover the much-desired open floor plan that seamlessly connects the rooms, allowing views to flow and creating an expansive and welcoming atmosphere. The open layout enhances the sense of space, making the home feel larger and more inviting.

A rear covered porch awaits, providing an ideal space for outdoor dining and relaxation. Whether enjoying a leisurely meal or unwinding with a book, this porch offers a perfect retreat to savor the outdoors while maintaining privacy and comfort.

The roof design features a stick construction with a main pitch of 9:12, showcasing both structural integrity and architectural appeal. This design element adds to the overall aesthetic of the home, complementing its Southern elegance.

Discover the elegance of simplicity with this one-story house plan, where thoughtful design meets practicality. From the steep hip roof to the ideal floor plan and the inviting covered porch, every aspect of this home has been carefully considered to create a space that combines style, functionality, and comfort.

REAR ELEVATION

Floor Plan

Main Level

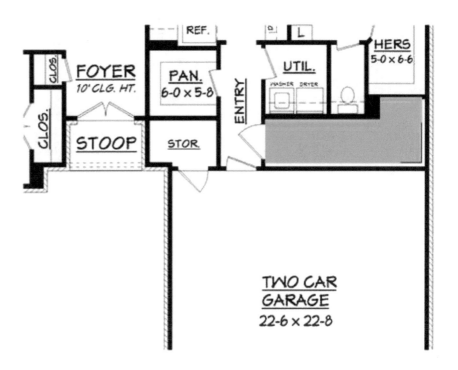

FOYER
10' CLG. HT.

CLOS.

CLOS.

STOOP

PAN.
6-0 x 5-8

STOR.

REF.

ENTRY

UTIL.

WASHER DRYER

HERS
5-0 x 6-6

TWO CAR
GARAGE
22-6 x 22-8

Plan details

Square Footage Breakdown
Total Heated Area:1,750 sq. ft.
1st Floor:1,750 sq. ft.
Storage:16 sq. ft.
Porch, Combined:132 sq. ft.
Beds/Baths
Bedrooms:3 or 4
Full Bathrooms:2
Foundation Type
Standard Foundations: Slab, Crawl
Optional Foundations: Basement, Walkout
Exterior Walls
Standard Type(s):2x4
Optional Type(s):2x6
Dimensions
Width:58' 4"
Depth:56' 8"
Max Ridge Height:22' 2"
Garage
Type: Attached
Area:541 sq. ft.
Count:2 cars
Entry Location: Front
Ceiling Heights
Floor / Height: Lower Level / 9' 4"First Floor / 9' 0"
Roof Details
Primary Pitch:9 on 12
Framing Type: Stick

Versatile and Spacious: A One-Story House Plan with 2 to 4 Bedrooms

Discover the versatility of this deceptively small one-story house plan, offering flexibility to accommodate your specific needs. With the option to choose between 2, 3, or 4 bedrooms, this home provides a customizable layout that adapts to your lifestyle.

Step inside and be greeted by high ceilings and an open floor plan that creates an immediate sense of spaciousness. The vaulted family room, complete with a cozy fireplace, seamlessly connects to the kitchen through a serving bar, allowing for effortless interaction and entertaining.

A bumped-out and vaulted breakfast nook provides a charming space for sunlit and tranquil meals. Whether it's enjoying a cup of coffee in the morning or savoring a leisurely brunch, this area offers a serene setting to start your day.

The master suite is thoughtfully positioned at the back of the home, ensuring privacy and tranquility. This secluded sanctuary offers a retreat from the rest of the house, providing a peaceful haven for relaxation and rest.

Two full baths are conveniently located to serve the additional bedrooms, offering comfort and convenience for family members or guests. Additionally, there is an optional fourth bedroom or the possibility to utilize the space as a versatile living room, giving you the freedom to tailor the design to your specific needs.

Experience the flexibility and spaciousness of this one-story house plan, where adaptability meets comfort. From the open floor plan and high ceilings to the master suite and optional bedrooms, every aspect of this home has been designed with versatility in mind. Embrace the opportunity to create a space that perfectly suits your lifestyle and preferences.

Floor Plan

Main Level

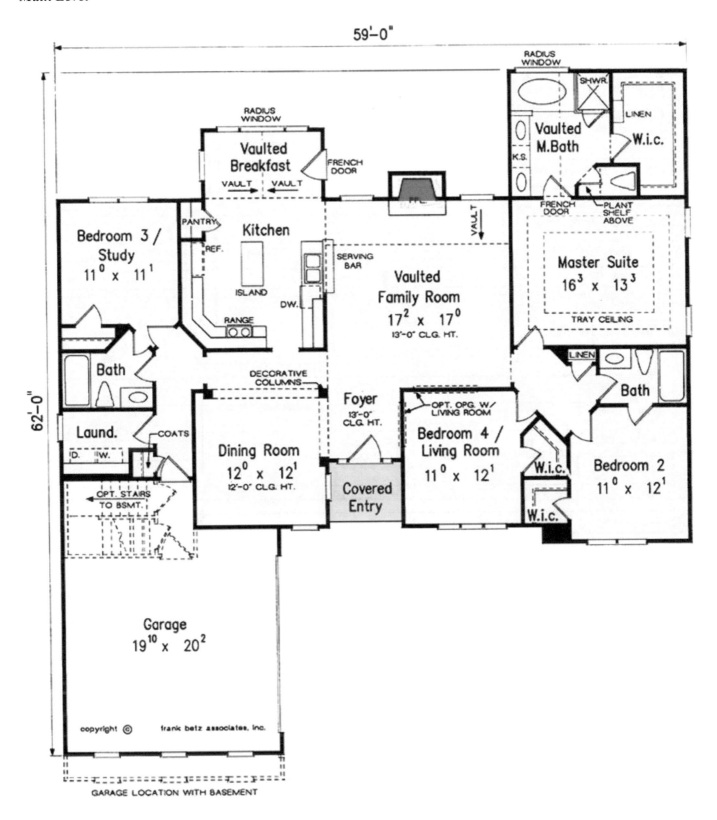

59'-0"

RADIUS WINDOW

SHWR.

Vaulted
M.Bath

LINEN

W.i.c.

K.S.

RADIUS WINDOW

Vaulted
Breakfast

FRENCH DOOR

VAULT   VAULT

PLANT SHELF ABOVE

FRENCH DOOR

VAULT

PANTRY

Kitchen

REF.

Bedroom 3 /
Study
11⁰ x 11¹

ISLAND

RANGE

DW.

SERVING BAR

Vaulted
Family Room
17² x 17⁰
13'-0" CLG. HT.

Master Suite
16³ x 13³

TRAY CEILING

Bath

62'-0"

Bath

LINEN

DECORATIVE COLUMNS

Foyer
13'-0" CLG. HT.

OPT. OPG. W/ LIVING ROOM

W.i.c.

Laund.

COATS

Dining Room
12⁰ x 12¹
12'-0" CLG. HT.

Bedroom 4 /
Living Room
11⁰ x 12¹

Bedroom 2
11⁰ x 12¹

D.   W.

OPT. STAIRS TO BSMT.

Covered
Entry

W.i.c.

Garage
19¹⁰ x 20²

copyright © frank betz associates, inc.

GARAGE LOCATION WITH BASEMENT

79

Plan details

Square Footage Breakdown
Total Heated Area:1,970 sq. ft.
1st Floor:1,970 sq. ft.
Beds/Baths
Bedrooms:2, 3, or 4
Full Bathrooms:3
Foundation Type
Standard Foundations: Crawl, Walkout
Exterior Walls
Standard Type(s):2x4
Dimensions
Width:59' 0"
Depth:64' 0"
Max Ridge Height:24' 0"
Garage
Type: Attached
Area:476 sq. ft.
Count:2 cars
Entry Location: Courtyard
Ceiling Heights
Floor / Height: First Floor / 9' 0"
Roof Details
Primary Pitch:10 on 12
Framing Type: Stick

Charming Country Craftsman: A One-Story House Plan with Vaulted Great Room

Experience the rustic charm of this one-story country Craftsman house plan, featuring a wide porch that spans the front of the home, providing ample outdoor space for enjoying the fresh air. At the back, a vaulted covered porch serves as an inviting outdoor living room, while a smaller porch area by the kitchen window offers additional outdoor enjoyment.

Step inside and be welcomed by an open floor plan adorned with a vaulted front-to-back ceiling, creating a sense of spaciousness and charm. The kitchen seamlessly connects to the vaulted dining room, creating a harmonious flow for entertaining and everyday living. The kitchen features a roomy corner pantry for storage and casual counter seating, perfect for quick meals or socializing. A side door provides convenient access for bringing groceries into the home, adding to the practicality of the design.

The master bedroom is a haven of natural light, boasting windows on three sides. It offers a large walk-in closet that can be accessed through a pocket door from the five-fixture bath, providing both functionality and privacy. The remaining bedrooms are located in the front corners of the home, and each comes with a linear closet, offering comfortable and private spaces for family members or guests.

The exterior finish of the home is specified for corrugated metal siding, adding to the rustic appeal and character of the design.

Embrace the charm and character of this one-story country Craftsman house plan, where indoor and outdoor living seamlessly blend. With its inviting porch spaces, vaulted great room, and well-designed layout, this home offers both style and functionality. Whether you're relaxing on the front porch, enjoying the outdoor living room, or appreciating the open and airy interior, this home is designed to enhance your lifestyle.

83

84

Floor Plan

Main Level

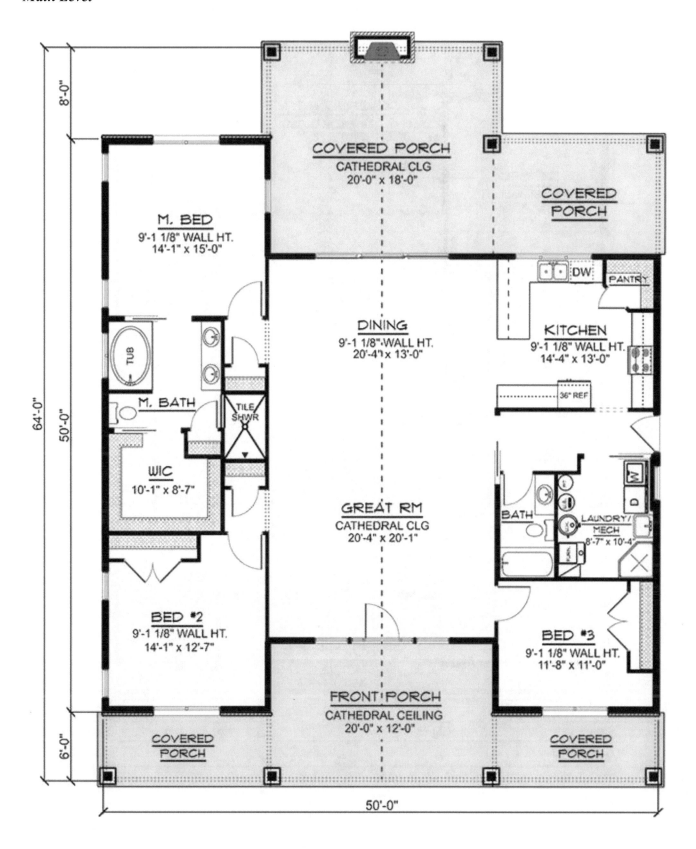

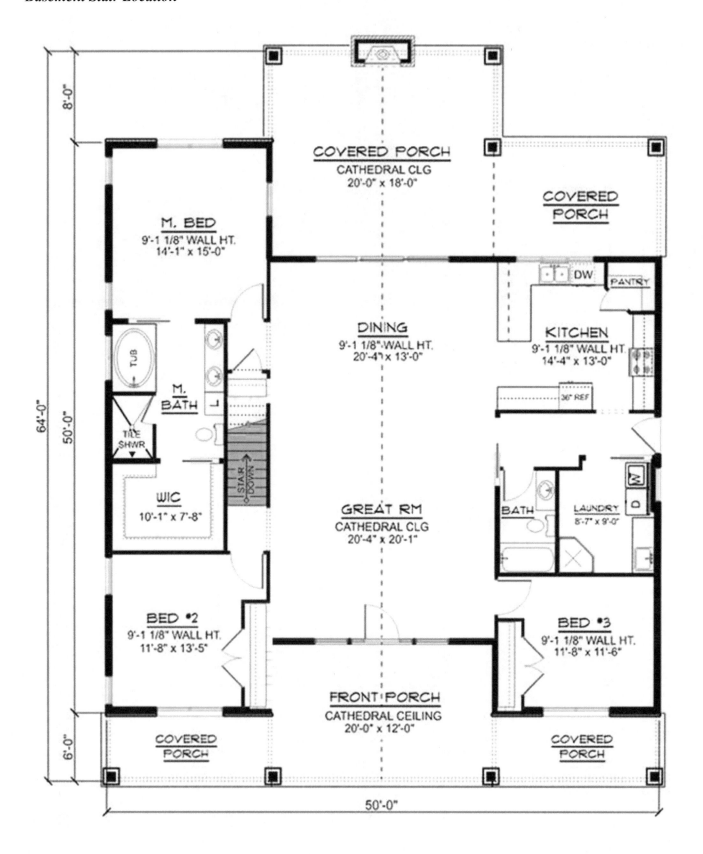

COVERED PORCH
CATHEDRAL CLG
20'-0" x 18'-0"

COVERED PORCH

M. BED
9'-1 1/8" WALL HT.
14'-1" x 15'-0"

DW

PANTRY

DINING
9'-1 1/8" WALL HT.
20'-4" x 13'-0"

KITCHEN
9'-1 1/8" WALL HT.
14'-4" x 13'-0"

TUB

36" REF

M. BATH

TILE SHWR

STAIR DOWN

WIC
10'-1" x 7'-8"

GREAT RM
CATHEDRAL CLG
20'-4" x 20'-1"

BATH

LAUNDRY
8'-7" x 9'-0"

W

D

BED #2
9'-1 1/8" WALL HT.
11'-8" x 13'-5"

BED #3
9'-1 1/8" WALL HT.
11'-8" x 11'-6"

FRONT PORCH
CATHEDRAL CEILING
20'-0" x 12'-0"

COVERED PORCH

COVERED PORCH

8'-0"

64'-0"

50'-0"

6'-0"

50'-0"

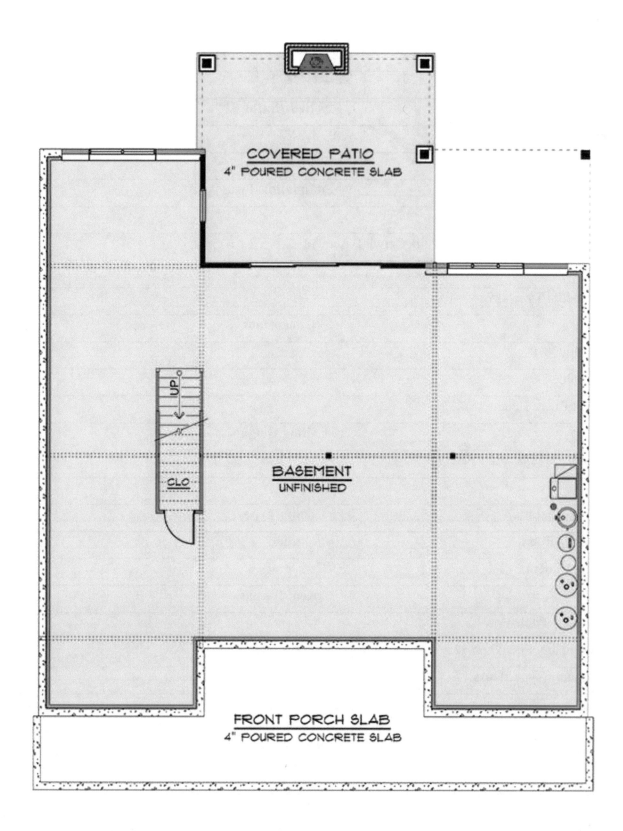

COVERED PATIO
4" POURED CONCRETE SLAB

UP

CLO

BASEMENT
UNFINISHED

FRONT PORCH SLAB
4" POURED CONCRETE SLAB

Plan details

Square Footage Breakdown	
Total Heated Area:2,030 sq. ft.	
1st Floor:2,030 sq. ft.	
Porch, Combined:939 sq. ft.	
Beds/Baths	
Bedrooms:3	
Full Bathrooms:2	
Foundation Type	
Standard Foundations: Slab	
Optional Foundations: Walkout, Crawl, Basement	
Exterior Walls	
Standard Type(s):2x6	
Dimensions	
Width:50' 0"	
Depth:64' 0"	
Max Ridge Height:18' 11"	
Ceiling Heights	
Floor / Height: First Floor / 9' 1"	
Room Details	**Ceiling Type**
Dining Room	Cathedral
Great Room	Cathedral
Roof Details	
Primary Pitch:4 on 12	
Secondary Pitch:5 on 12	
Framing Type: Truss	

Traditional Charm: A Spacious One-Story Home Design Under 2100 Sq Ft with Garage and Workshop

Discover the timeless appeal of this traditional one-story home design, perfectly suited for a wide or corner lot. This thoughtfully crafted design features a three-bay garage with a generous workshop area, a convenient storage space, and a half bath, providing both functionality and convenience.

Step inside and experience the well-planned split-bedroom design, which places the master suite in its own private wing. The master suite boasts twin walk-in closets, offering ample storage space. The luxurious master bath features a whirlpool tub and a glass-door shower, providing a spa-like retreat within the comfort of your own home.

The expansive living area showcases built-in bookshelves, adding a touch of elegance and practicality. A bayed breakfast nook and an open kitchen are additional highlights of this inviting space, creating a warm and welcoming atmosphere for everyday living and entertaining.

At the back of the home, a covered porch extends the living space to the outdoors, providing a perfect spot for relaxation and enjoying nature.

Ceilings throughout the home are 8 feet high as standard, creating an open and airy ambiance. In select areas such as the great room, dining room, and master bedroom, the ceilings are boxed and raised to 9 feet, adding a touch of grandeur and architectural interest.

Experience the traditional charm of this one-story home design, where comfort and practicality are blended seamlessly. From the spacious garage and workshop area to the master suite and expansive living area, every aspect of this home has been thoughtfully designed to enhance your lifestyle. Enjoy the convenience of a well-appointed home while embracing the timeless elegance of traditional design..

Covered rear porch with door shown going to the Great Room

Kitchen with dining room viewed in background

Kitchen shown with optional island

REAR ELEVATION

LEFT ELEVATION

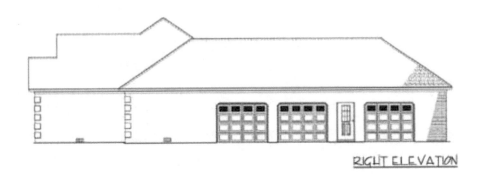

RIGHT ELEVATION

Floor Plan

Main Level

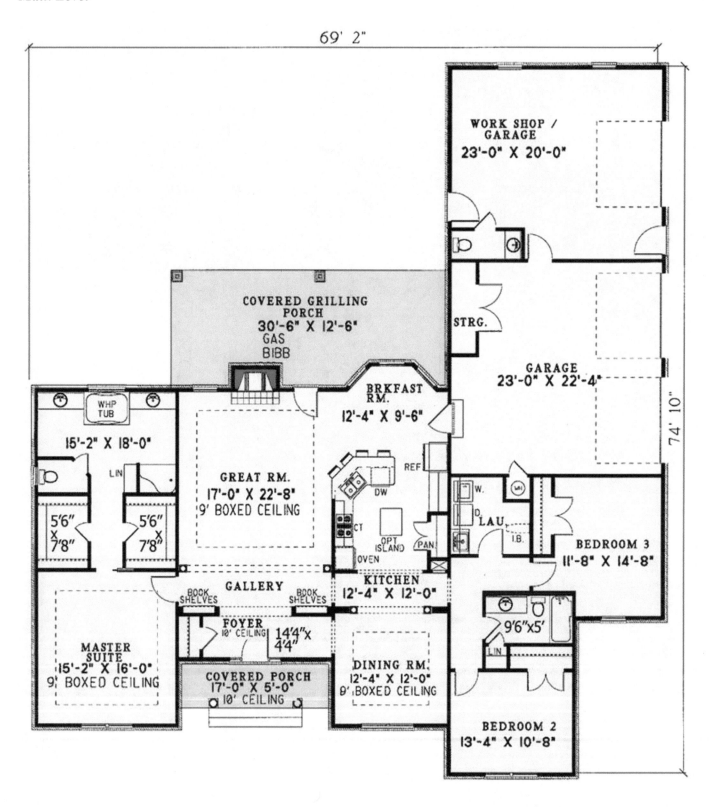

Plan details

Square Footage Breakdown
Total Heated Area:2,096 sq. ft.
1st Floor:2,096 sq. ft.
Porch, Rear:397 sq. ft.
Porch, Front:85 sq. ft.
Beds/Baths
Bedrooms:3
Full Bathrooms:2
Half Bathrooms:1
Foundation Type
Standard Foundations: Slab, Crawl
Optional Foundations: Basement, Walkout
Exterior Walls
Standard Type(s):2x4
Optional Type(s):2x6
Dimensions
Width:69' 2"
Depth:74' 10"
Max Ridge Height:20' 4"
Garage
Type: Attached
Area:974 sq. ft.
Count:3 cars
Entry Location: Side
Ceiling Heights
Floor / Height: First Floor / 8' 0"
Roof Details
Primary Pitch:8 on 12
Secondary Pitch:4.5 on 12
Framing Type: Stick

Spacious Rustic Craftsman: A 3000 Square Foot One-Story House Plan with Flex Room

Embrace the rustic charm of this spacious one-story Craftsman house plan, offering 3 bedrooms and 3,007 square feet of heated living space. With a 3-car courtyard-entry garage, this home combines functionality and style to create a comfortable and inviting living environment.

Enter the home through either the 3-car garage or the covered porch, providing convenient access points. Inside, a formal dining room with a 12' ceiling is easily accessible, leading to a walk-in pantry and straight ahead to the kitchen. As you proceed from the entry, the vaulted great room with expansive view windows opens up, offering a breathtaking vista of the backyard. A large covered porch extends from the great room, providing an ideal space for outdoor relaxation and entertainment.

A gourmet kitchen is nearby, featuring an oversized island and ample cabinet space, eliminating any stress associated with food storage and preparation. A casual eating nook tucked away in the back left corner overlooks the backyard and covered porch, creating a cozy spot for enjoying meals.

The left wing of the home comprises two spacious guest bedrooms, an oversized utility room, and a shared full bathroom. Additionally, a powder room is conveniently located along the same hallway leading to the utility room.

On the opposite side of the home, you'll discover two versatile flex spaces along with the fully featured primary bedroom suite. A cozy flex room complements a larger den just across the hallway, both of which can easily serve as additional guest bedrooms or multipurpose areas. The primary bedroom boasts a vaulted ceiling, a generous walk-in closet, a private covered porch, and a separate tub and shower. The access to the porch not only provides a serene outdoor space but also floods the room with natural light.

Experience the spaciousness and rustic beauty of this one-story Craftsman house plan, where style meets practicality. From the open and inviting living areas to the private primary suite and versatile flex spaces, this home offers both comfort and flexibility. Enjoy the charm of rustic living while indulging in modern conveniences and amenities.

Floor Plan

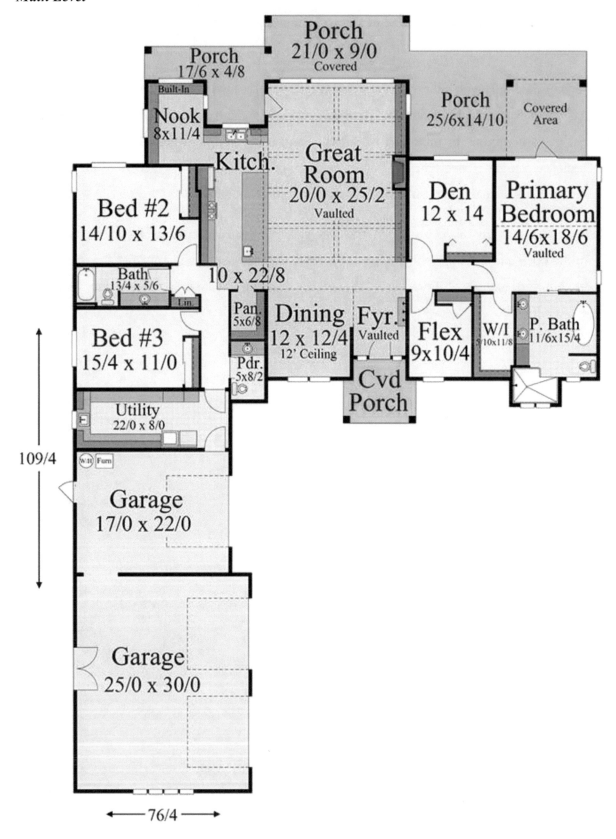

Porch
21/0 x 9/0
Covered

Porch
17/6 x 4/8

Built-In

Nook
8x11/4

Porch
25/6x14/10

Covered
Area

Kitch.

Great
Room
20/0 x 25/2
Vaulted

Den
12 x 14

Primary
Bedroom
14/6x18/6
Vaulted

Bed #2
14/10 x 13/6

Bath
13/4 x 5/6

Lin.

10 x 22/8

Pan.
5x6/8

Dining
12 x 12/4
12' Ceiling

Fyr.
Vaulted

Flex
9x10/4

W/I
5/10x11/8

P. Bath
11/6x15/4

Bed #3
15/4 x 11/0

Pdr.
5x8/2

Cvd
Porch

Utility
22/0 x 8/0

W/H Furn

109/4

Garage
17/0 x 22/0

Garage
25/0 x 30/0

76/4

Plan details

Square Footage Breakdown	
Total Heated Area:3,007 sq. ft.	
1st Floor:3,007 sq. ft.	
Beds/Baths	
Bedrooms:3, 4, or 5	
Full Bathrooms:2	
Half Bathrooms:1	
Foundation Type	
Standard Foundations: Crawl	
Optional Foundations: Walkout, Slab, Basement	
Exterior Walls	
Standard Type(s):2x6	
Dimensions	
Width:76' 4"	
Depth:109' 4"	
Garage	
Type: Attached	
Count:3 cars	
Entry Location: Courtyard	

Elegant Transitional Living: A 2500 Square Foot One-Story House Plan with 3-Car Garage

Experience the perfect blend of modern elegance and transitional design in this one-story house plan. With a covered entry and a side entry garage, complemented by tall peaks, this home exudes charm and curb appeal. The attractive brick exterior, adorned with timber lintels above the windows, adds to its visual appeal.

As you step through the front covered entry, you are welcomed by high ceilings in the foyer, creating a sense of grandeur. Continue into the great room, where vaulted ceilings and a tall fireplace await. A large sliding glass door leads to the 15'10"-deep covered porch at the back, seamlessly integrating indoor and outdoor living spaces. The great room flows effortlessly into the kitchen, which boasts a large eat-at island and a hidden walk-in pantry, combining functionality and style.

The master suite is a luxurious retreat, featuring vaulted ceilings and offering stunning views to the back through a large picture window. Enter through a sliding barn door into the spacious master bathroom, which showcases a double vanity, a walk-in tile shower, a freestanding tub, and a private toilet room. Additionally, a large walk-in closet provides direct access to the laundry area, enhancing convenience and efficiency.

On the opposite side of the home, you'll find two additional bedrooms, each with its own private bathroom, offering comfort and privacy for family members or guests.

Indulge in the elegance and comfort of this transitional one-story house plan, where stylish design elements and thoughtful features create a harmonious living environment. From the inviting entryway and spacious great room to the luxurious master suite and well-appointed bedrooms, every aspect of this home has been carefully designed for both aesthetics and functionality. Embrace modern living while enjoying the timeless appeal of transitional architecture.

108

Floor Plan

Main Level

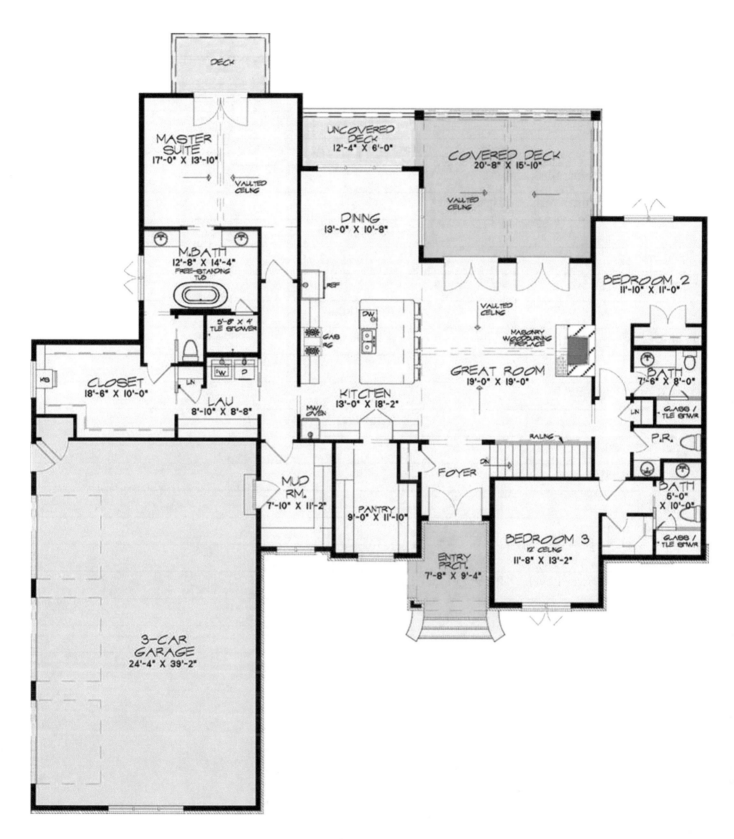

Plan details

Square Footage Breakdown	
Total Heated Area:2,515 sq. ft.	
1st Floor:2,515 sq. ft.	
Porch, Combined:390 sq. ft.	
Beds/Baths	
Bedrooms:3	
Full Bathrooms:3	
Half Bathrooms:1	
Foundation Type	
Standard Foundations: Slab, Crawl	
Optional Foundations: Walkout, Basement	
Exterior Walls	
Standard Type(s):2x4	
Optional Type(s):2x6	
Dimensions	
Width:74' 8"	
Depth:83' 4"	
Max Ridge Height:27' 0"	
Garage	
Type: Attached	
Area:1010 sq. ft.	
Count:3 cars	
Entry Location: Side	
Ceiling Heights	
Floor / Height: Lower Level / 9' 0"First Floor / 10' 0"	
Roof Details	
Primary Pitch:10 on 12	

Mountain Retreat: A One-Story Craftsman House Plan with 3-Car Garage

Discover the allure of mountain living with this charming one-story Craftsman house plan. Boasting 4 bedrooms, 3 baths, and 2454 square feet of heated living space, this home offers a flexible layout, including a versatile flex room and a den, as well as a thoughtfully designed split bedroom arrangement to maximize privacy and comfort.

Step into the expansive interior of this mountain retreat, where attention to detail creates a warm and inviting atmosphere. The open-concept design seamlessly integrates the living spaces, allowing for effortless flow and functionality.

Out back, a spacious covered patio with a cozy fireplace extends your living area, providing the perfect setting for outdoor relaxation and entertainment, while embracing the natural beauty of the surrounding mountain landscape.

The master suite is a haven of tranquility, featuring a large walk-in closet with convenient direct access to the laundry area. On the opposite side of the home, Bedrooms 2 and 3 share a Jack and Jill bathroom, ensuring comfort and convenience for family members or guests.

Adding to the versatility of this home, a flex room, in addition to a den, offers endless possibilities. Whether utilized as a home office, a hobby space, or a playroom, this room provides the flexibility to adapt to your unique needs and lifestyle.

Embrace the serenity and beauty of mountain living with this one-story Craftsman house plan. From the flexible layout and private bedroom arrangement to the inviting outdoor living space, every aspect of this home has been thoughtfully designed to enhance your comfort and enjoyment. Create lasting memories in this mountain retreat, where modern amenities meet rustic charm.

FRONT ELEVATION

LEFT ELEVATION

REAR ELEVATION

RIGHT ELEVATION

Floor Plan

Main Level

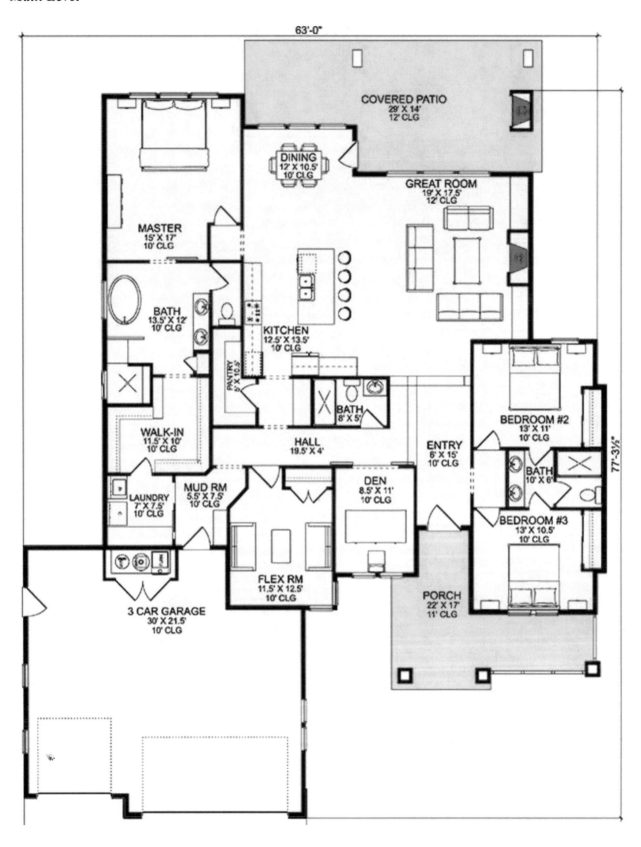

Plan details

Square Footage Breakdown
Total Heated Area:2,454 sq. ft.
1st Floor:2,454 sq. ft.
Covered Patio:252 sq. ft.
Porch, Front:204 sq. ft.
Beds/Baths
Bedrooms:4
Full Bathrooms:3
Foundation Type
Standard Foundations: Slab, Crawl
Optional Foundations: Basement
Exterior Walls
Standard Type(s):2x6
Dimensions
Width:64' 0"
Depth:81' 6"
Garage
Type: Attached
Area:805 sq. ft.
Count:3 cars
Entry Location: Front
Ceiling Heights
Floor / Height: First Floor / 10' 0"
Roof Details
Primary Pitch:8 on 12
Secondary Pitch:6 on 12
Framing Type: Stick And Truss

Contemporary Charm: A New American House Plan with Flex and Bonus Rooms

Experience contemporary elegance with this stunning New American house plan. Featuring an attractive exterior adorned with board and batten siding and stone trim, this home is sure to catch the eye. Step inside to discover 1737 square feet of heated living space, accompanied by 540 square feet of bonus expansion, and a 2-car 408 square foot garage.

As you enter, a versatile flex room awaits, offering endless possibilities. Whether utilized as a home office, a den, or even a third bedroom, this room adapts to your specific needs and lifestyle, ensuring flexibility and convenience.

Architectural Designs' website presents an extensive collection of home designs, encompassing various architectural styles, sizes, and features. We understand the importance of personalization, and our designs can be customized to meet your specific preferences and requirements.

We are committed to curating and expanding our design portfolio every day, collaborating with numerous residential building designers and architects. This dedication enables us to provide you with the most diverse and exceptional house plans available, ensuring that your dream home becomes a reality.

Discover contemporary charm and exceptional design with this New American house plan. From the striking exterior to the versatile interior spaces, this home offers both style and functionality. Explore the endless possibilities and customization options available through Architectural Designs, and let us help you create the perfect home that reflects your unique taste and lifestyle.

REAR ELEVATION

Floor Plan

Main Level

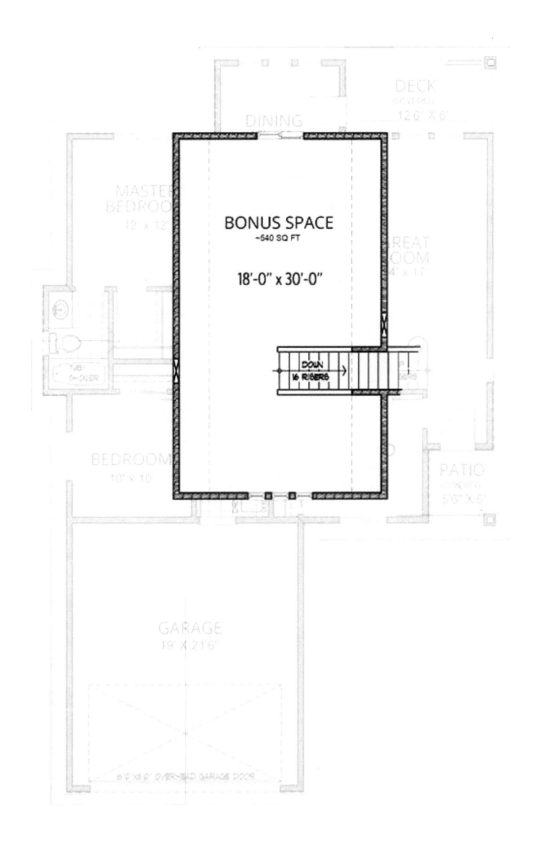

BONUS SPACE
~540 SQ FT

18'-0" x 30'-0"

DOWN
16 RISERS

DINING

DECK
12'6" X 6'

MASTER
BEDROOM
12' x 12'

GREAT
ROOM

BEDROOM
10' x 10'

PATIO
5'6" X 6'

GARAGE
19' X 21'6'

Plan details

Square Footage Breakdown
Total Heated Area:1,737 sq. ft.
1st Floor:1,197 sq. ft.
Covered Patio:33 sq. ft.
Deck:75 sq. ft.
Bonus:540 sq. ft.
Beds/Baths
Bedrooms:2 or 3
Full Bathrooms:2
Foundation Type
Standard Foundations: Crawl
Exterior Walls
Standard Type(s):2x6
Dimensions
Width:38' 0"
Depth:60' 0"
Max Ridge Height:21' 10"
Garage
Type: Attached
Area:408 sq. ft.
Count:2 cars
Entry Location: Front
Ceiling Heights
Floor / Height: First Floor / 9' 0"BONUS ROOM 8' 0"
Roof Details
Primary Pitch:8 on 12
Framing Type: Stick

Mountain Ranch Retreat: A Spacious One-Story Home with Customization Options

Escape to the tranquility of mountain living with this exquisite one-story ranch home. Featuring beautiful decorative wood trim on the exterior, this residence blends rustic charm with modern comfort. Step inside and be greeted by wide open spaces, as the vaulted and beamed great room becomes the focal point from the moment you enter the foyer.

The interior of this home is designed to maximize space and views. Half walls maintain an open flow throughout, while interior columns and special ceiling treatments add elegance and character to the living areas.

The kitchen is a chef's dream, offering two islands, a spacious walk-in pantry, and an abundance of counter space for all your culinary needs. Prepare meals with ease while enjoying the mountain views that surround you.

A two-sided fireplace serves as a focal point, creating a cozy ambiance shared between the great room and the hearth room. Whether you're entertaining guests or enjoying a quiet evening at home, this feature adds warmth and charm to your living space.

The split bedroom layout provides privacy and separation, with the master suite serving as a private oasis. Retreat to your own sanctuary, separate from the other bedrooms, and indulge in the serenity of mountain living.

Experience the ultimate mountain ranch retreat with this spacious one-story home. From the beautiful wood trim on the exterior to the open and inviting interior spaces, this residence offers the perfect blend of rustic charm and modern luxury. Customize this design to suit your specific needs and preferences, and create a home that embodies your unique style. Embrace the beauty of mountain living and enjoy a private oasis in this exceptional retreat.

124

FRONT ELEVATION

LEFT ELEVATION

REAR ELEVATION

RIGHT ELEVATION

Floor Plan

Main Level

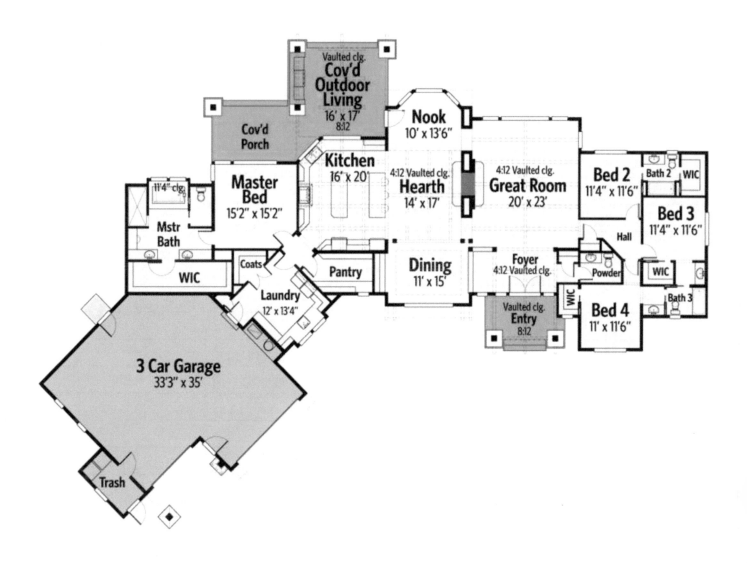

Plan details

Square Footage Breakdown
Total Heated Area:3,270 sq. ft.
1st Floor:3,270 sq. ft.
Beds/Baths
Bedrooms:4
Full Bathrooms:3
Half Bathrooms:1
Foundation Type
Standard Foundations: Crawl
Exterior Walls
Standard Type(s):2x6
Dimensions
Width:124' 0"
Depth:88' 0"
Max Ridge Height:23' 0"
Garage
Type: Attached
Area:1160 sq. ft.
Count:3 cars
Entry Location: Front, Courtyard
Ceiling Heights
Floor / Height: First Floor / 9' 0"
Roof Details
Primary Pitch:8 on 12
Framing Type: Truss

Efficient and Stylish: A One-Story Barndominium-Style House Plan with Expansive Wrap-Around Porch

Experience the perfect blend of efficiency and style with this one-story Barndominium-style house plan. Designed with a simple shape, this home offers ease of construction without compromising on aesthetics. The standout feature is the 9'-deep wrap-around porch, providing ample outdoor space for relaxation and entertainment.

Step inside and be greeted by a wide-open floor plan that exudes spaciousness. The soaring cathedral ceiling and 14' high walls create an airy and grand atmosphere. The focal point of the great room is a beautiful corner fireplace, adding warmth and charm to the living space.

The kitchen is a chef's delight, featuring a large walk-in pantry and an island with a convenient snack bar. Prepare meals with ease while enjoying the seamless flow between the kitchen and the rest of the living area. An office is thoughtfully located right off the main living space, providing a dedicated workspace or study area.

The master bedroom is situated on the right side of the home, offering privacy and tranquility. The master bathroom boasts his/her vanities, a linen closet, and an enclosed toilet area, providing functionality and convenience. Bedrooms 2 and 3 share a conveniently located hall bathroom, ensuring comfort for family members or guests.

The highlight of this house plan is the massive garage, which includes three doors and ample space for hobbies or car collections. Whether you need room for storage, a workshop, or your prized vehicles, this garage has you covered.

Embrace the efficiency and style of the Barndominium lifestyle with this one-story house plan. From the efficient design and expansive wrap-around porch to the well-appointed interior spaces, this home offers a perfect balance of functionality and charm. Customize this plan to suit your specific needs and make it your own. Enjoy the convenience of a spacious garage while relishing the outdoor living space provided by the impressive wrap-around porch.

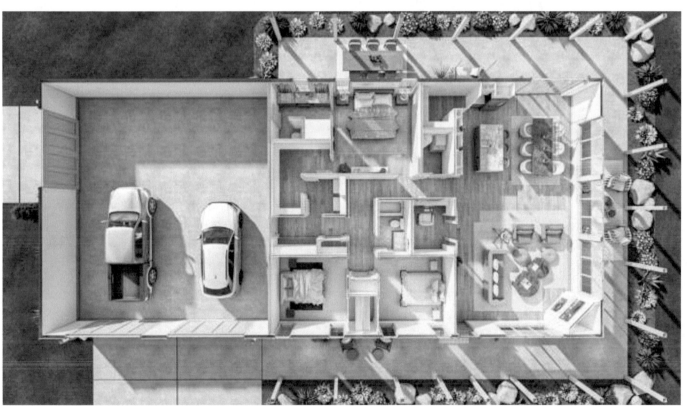

Floor Plan

Main Level

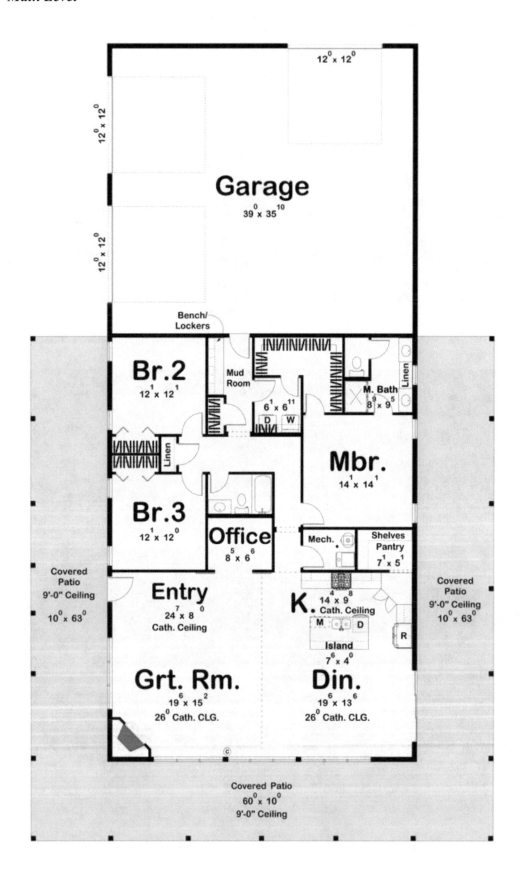

Plan details

Square Footage Breakdown
Total Heated Area:2,113 sq. ft.
1st Floor:2,113 sq. ft.
Porch, Combined:1,667 sq. ft.
Beds/Baths
Bedrooms:3
Full Bathrooms:2
Foundation Type
Standard Foundations: Slab
Optional Foundations: Walkout, Crawl, Basement
Exterior Walls
Standard Type(s):2x6
Dimensions
Width:60' 0"
Depth:100' 0"
Garage
Type: Attached
Area:1453 sq. ft.
Count:1, 2, or 3 cars
Entry Location: Side, Rear
Ceiling Heights
Floor / Height: First Floor / 14' 0"
Roof Details
Primary Pitch:10 on 12
Secondary Pitch:3 on 12
Framing Type: Truss

One-Story Wonder House Plan with Impressive Features

Step into the world of one-story wonder with this exceptional house plan. From the inviting covered front porch, you'll enter into a home that boasts 13' ceilings in the foyer and great room, creating a sense of grandeur. The addition of a coat closet helps keep the entryway clutter-free.

The heart of this home is the spacious great room, which features a fireplace on the far wall and is framed by windows that offer stunning views of the screened porch. The open layout seamlessly connects the great room, kitchen, and breakfast room, providing a sense of openness and flow.

The kitchen is a chef's dream, complete with a large walk-in pantry to keep your essentials organized. Enjoy casual meals at the counter or in the breakfast area, and take advantage of the screened porch for al fresco dining. For more formal occasions, a separate dining room is conveniently located nearby, ensuring a tranquil setting away from kitchen activity.

The master suite is a retreat in itself, featuring a double tray ceiling and side-by-side walk-in closets. The laundry area is conveniently located nearby, adding to the overall functionality and convenience of this home.

Two additional bedrooms are thoughtfully situated across the home, offering privacy and comfort for family members or guests. Additionally, a study off the foyer provides a private retreat, ideal for a home office or a quiet space to unwind. Discover the wonders of one-story living with this impressive house plan. From the grand entrance and open living spaces to the well-appointed master suite and private study, every aspect of this home has been carefully designed to enhance your comfort and enjoyment. Customize this plan to fit your unique needs and make it your own. Experience the convenience of a thoughtfully laid out floor plan that maximizes privacy and functionality, creating a harmonious living environment.

148

REAR ELEVATION

151

Floor Plan

Plan details

Square Footage Breakdown
Total Heated Area:2,310 sq. ft.
1st Floor:2,310 sq. ft.
Screened Porch:200 sq. ft.
Beds/Baths
Bedrooms:3
Full Bathrooms:3
Foundation Type
Standard Foundations: Crawl, Basement
Exterior Walls
Standard Type(s):2x4
Dimensions
Width:72' 8"
Depth:47' 8"
Max Ridge Height:27' 0"
Garage
Type: Attached
Area:506 sq. ft.
Count:2 cars
Entry Location: Side
Ceiling Heights
Floor / Height: First Floor / 9' 0"
Roof Details
Primary Pitch:12 on 12
Framing Type: Stick

Comfortable and Charming: A One-Story Country Craftsman Home Plan with Loft and Optional Bonus Room

Experience the perfect blend of comfort and charm with this exceptional one-story Country Craftsman home plan. Designed with a comfortable layout suitable for families of any size, this home offers tall ceilings and an open concept living space that seamlessly flows onto a covered veranda.

As you enter the foyer, you'll be greeted by a formal dining room on one side and a quiet study on the other, providing versatile spaces for relaxation and entertainment. Towards the rear of the home, tall ceilings create a sense of spaciousness, and the open kitchen offers ample workspace and a convenient pass-through pantry for maximum storage.

The master suite is privately tucked away behind the 2-car garage, providing a peaceful retreat. It features a luxurious 5-fixture bath and a roomy walk-in closet, catering to your comfort and storage needs. On the opposite side of the home, two additional bedrooms share a Jack and Jill bath, ensuring privacy and convenience for family members or guests.

A powder bath is conveniently located just inside from the double garage, offering added convenience for everyday living. Next to the garage, you'll find a well-appointed laundry room, making chores a breeze.

For additional space and versatility, you have the option to expand upstairs. The second floor offers a loft, a bonus room, and a game room, adding an extra 540 square feet to the home when finished as shown. This area can be customized to suit your specific needs, whether it be a playroom, a home office, or a media room.

Discover the comfort and charm of this one-story Country Craftsman home plan. From the inviting open living spaces and well-appointed master suite to the optional loft and bonus room, this home offers a perfect blend of functionality and style. Customize this plan to suit your unique needs and create a space that reflects your personal taste. Embrace the warmth and character of country living while enjoying the convenience and versatility of a thoughtfully designed floor plan.

159

REAR ELEVATION - WALKOUT FOUNDATION

Floor Plan

Main Level

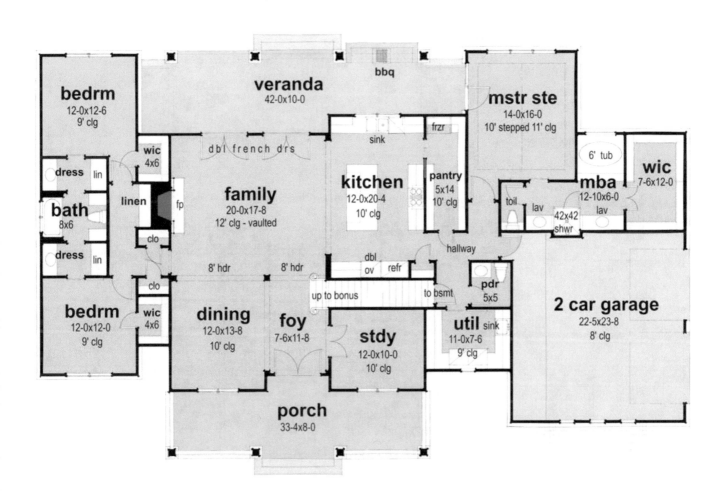

2nd Floor

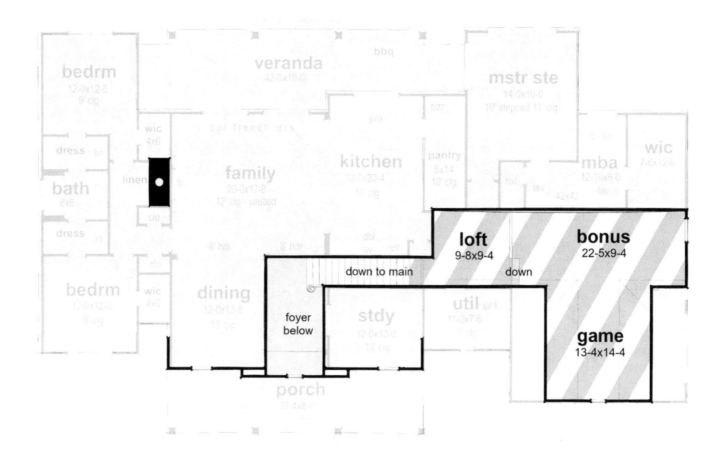

bedrm
12-0x12-6
9' clg

dress   lin

bath
8x6

dress   lin

bedrm
12-0x12-0
9' clg

wic
4x6

linen

clo

wic
4x0

clo

veranda
42-0x10-0

bbq

dpl french drs

family
20-0x17-8
12' clg - vaulted

8' hdr

8' hdr

dining
12-0x13-8
10' clg

foyer
below

kitchen
12-0x20-4
10' clg

sink

pantry
6x14
10' clg

dbl
ov   ref

stdy
12-0x10-0
10' clg

mstr ste
14-0x16-0
10' stepped 11' clg

wic
7-6x12-0

mba
12-10x6-0

lav

toil   lav

42x42

loft
9-8x9-4

down to main

bonus
22-5x9-4

down

util sink
11-0x7-6
9' clg

game
13-4x14-4

porch
13-4x8-0

Walkout Foundation Option

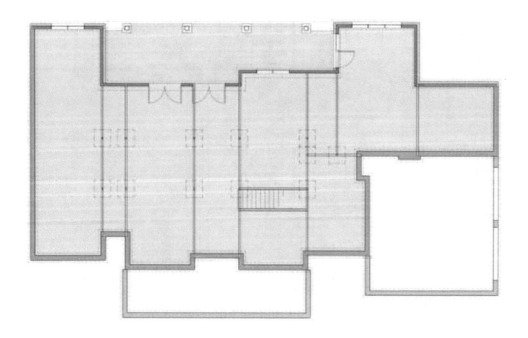

Plan details

Square Footage Breakdown
Total Heated Area:2,510 sq. ft.
1st Floor:2,510 sq. ft.
Porch, Combined:650 sq. ft.
Porch, Rear:367 sq. ft.
Porch, Front:283 sq. ft.
Bonus:540 sq. ft.
Basement Unfinished:2,510 sq. ft.

Beds/Baths
Bedrooms:3
Full Bathrooms:2
Half Bathrooms:1

Foundation Type
Standard Foundations: Crawl, Monolithic Slab
Optional Foundations: Basement, Walkout

Exterior Walls
Standard Type(s):2x4
Optional Type(s):2x6

Dimensions
Width:84' 11"
Depth:51' 7"
Max Ridge Height:30' 2"

Garage
Type: Attached
Area:550 sq. ft.
Count:2 or 3 cars
Entry Location: Front, Side

Ceiling Heights
Floor / Height: First Floor / 10' 0"Bonus 9' 0"

Room Details	Ceiling Type	Height
Family Room	Vaulted	12' 0" to 16' 0"

Roof Details
Primary Pitch:12 on 12
Secondary Pitch:4 on 12
Framing Type:Stick

Versatile Lake or Mountain House Plan Under 1700 Square Feet with Stunning Rear Deck

Discover the perfect home for your rear-sloping lot with this versatile lake or mountain house plan. Designed to maximize the beauty of the back side, this home features a captivating rear deck and an expandable layout that offers ample space for your needs.

This house plan is all about the back side, where the true beauty unfolds. As you enter, the ceiling slopes up, drawing your attention towards the breathtaking two-story wall of windows. From here, you can enjoy panoramic views across the 15'-deep covered deck, making it the perfect spot to take in the serene surroundings.

The bedrooms are thoughtfully located on either side of the entry, ensuring privacy and comfort. Each bedroom is equipped with a walk-in closet and its own bathroom, providing convenience and luxury for everyone in the household.

The lower level of this home offers a generous 1,720 square feet of expansion space. Here, you'll find a third bedroom and bathroom, allowing for additional living space or guest accommodations. This area can be customized to suit your specific needs, whether it be a recreation room, a home office, or a gym.

Experience the beauty and versatility of this lake or mountain house plan, perfectly designed for a rear-sloping lot. From the captivating rear deck to the well-appointed bedrooms and expandable lower level, every aspect of this home has been carefully considered to provide comfort, functionality, and breathtaking views. Customize this plan to fit your unique needs and create the perfect retreat that complements your lifestyle. Embrace the serenity of lake or mountain living while enjoying the convenience and flexibility of an expandable floor plan.

Floor Plan

Main Level

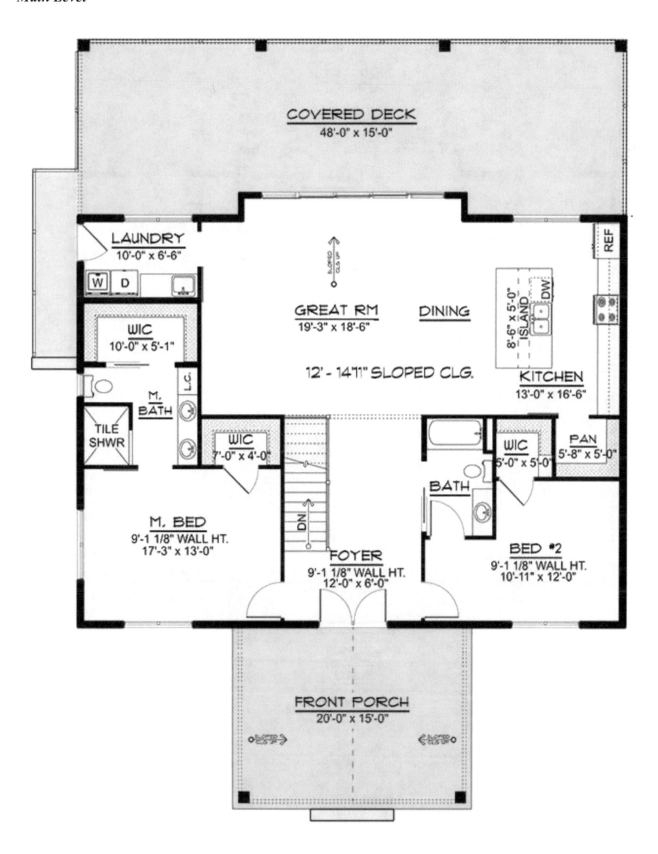

COVERED DECK
48'-0" x 15'-0"

LAUNDRY
10'-0" x 6'-6"

W   D

REF

SLOPED CLG UP

GREAT RM
19'-3" x 18'-6"

DINING

8'-6" x 5'-0"
ISLAND

DW

WIC
10'-0" x 5'-1"

12' - 14'11" SLOPED CLG.

KITCHEN
13'-0" x 16'-6"

L.C.

M.
BATH

WIC
7'-0" x 4'-0"

WIC
5'-0" x 5'-0"

PAN
5'-8" x 5'-0"

TILE
SHWR

BATH

M. BED
9'-1 1/8" WALL HT.
17'-3" x 13'-0"

DN

FOYER
9'-1 1/8" WALL HT.
12'-0" x 6'-0"

BED #2
9'-1 1/8" WALL HT.
10'-11" x 12'-0"

FRONT PORCH
20'-0" x 15'-0"

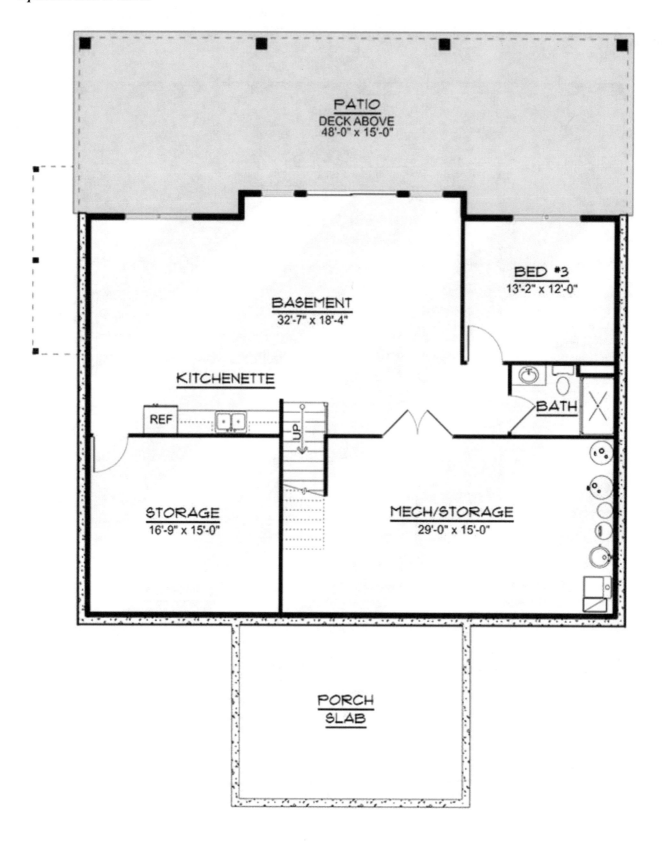

PATIO
DECK ABOVE
48'-0" x 15'-0"

BED #3
13'-2" x 12'-0"

BASEMENT
32'-7" x 18'-4"

KITCHENETTE

REF

BATH

UP

STORAGE
16'-9" x 15'-0"

MECH/STORAGE
29'-0" x 15'-0"

PORCH
SLAB

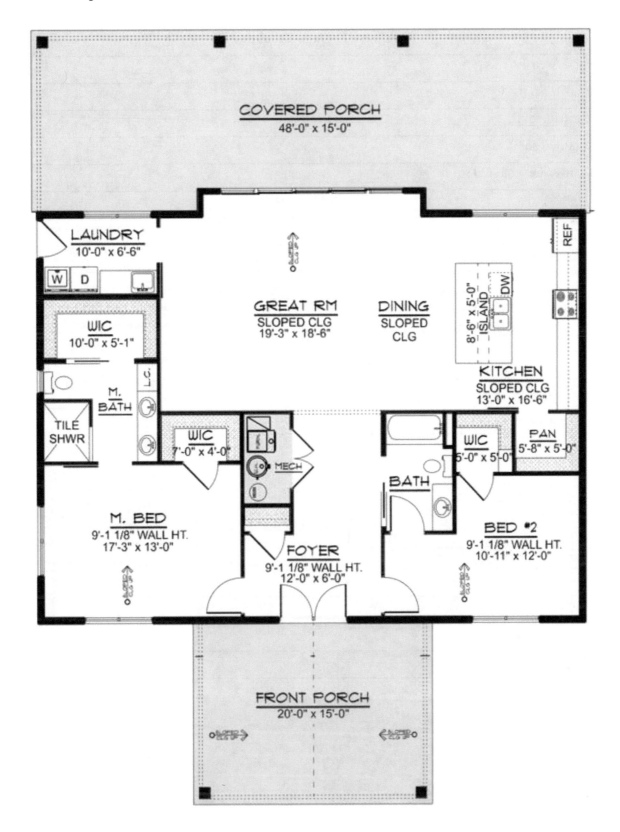

Plan details

Square Footage Breakdown
Total Heated Area:1,679 sq. ft.
1st Floor:1,679 sq. ft.
Porch, Rear:657 sq. ft.
Porch, Front:300 sq. ft.
Optional Lower Level:1,720 sq. ft.
Beds/Baths
Bedrooms:2 or 3
Full Bathrooms:2 or 3
Foundation Type
Standard Foundations:Walkout
Optional Foundations:Slab, Crawl, Basement
Exterior Walls
Standard Type(s):2x6
Dimensions
Width:52' 0"
Depth:65' 0"
Max Ridge Height:18' 10"
Ceiling Heights
Floor / Height:Lower Level / 9' 0"First Floor / 9' 0"
Roof Details
Primary Pitch:2 on 12
Secondary Pitch:6 on 12
Framing Type:Stick

Charming Traditional House Plan with Three Bedrooms and a Spacious 2-Car Garage

Welcome to this charming traditional house plan, offering three bedrooms, two bathrooms, and a thoughtfully designed layout that maximizes both comfort and functionality. With 1,658 square feet of heated living space and a generous 498 square foot 2-car garage, this home caters to your family's needs.

As you enter, you'll be greeted by an inviting open concept great room that seamlessly combines the living, dining, and kitchen areas. Large windows flood the space with natural light, creating an airy and bright atmosphere. Whether you're hosting family gatherings or enjoying intimate moments, this versatile layout accommodates every occasion.

The kitchen is a chef's delight, featuring an island with seating and ample prep space. A double sink is perfectly positioned below a window, offering a pleasant view of the backyard. Additionally, a convenient walk-in pantry provides ample storage for your kitchen essentials, keeping everything organized and within reach.

The three bedrooms are thoughtfully arranged in a split layout, ensuring privacy and tranquility for everyone. Each bedroom is filled with natural light, creating a warm and inviting ambiance.

The attached 2-car garage not only provides shelter for your vehicles but also offers valuable storage space for your outdoor gear, tools, or hobby equipment. Stay organized and keep your belongings protected in this functional addition to the home.

Embrace the charm and functionality of this traditional house plan, featuring three bedrooms, an open concept great room, and a spacious 2-car garage. From the inviting living spaces to the well-appointed kitchen and tranquil bedrooms, every aspect of this home has been carefully designed to enhance your comfort and enjoyment. Customize this plan to suit your unique needs and create a space that reflects your personal style. Experience the convenience and practicality of a thoughtfully laid out floor plan, providing a harmonious living environment for you and your loved ones.

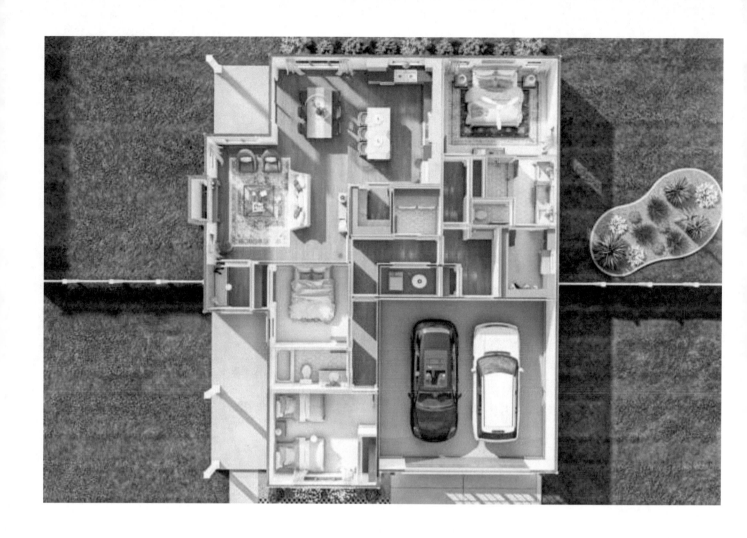

Floor Plan

Main Level

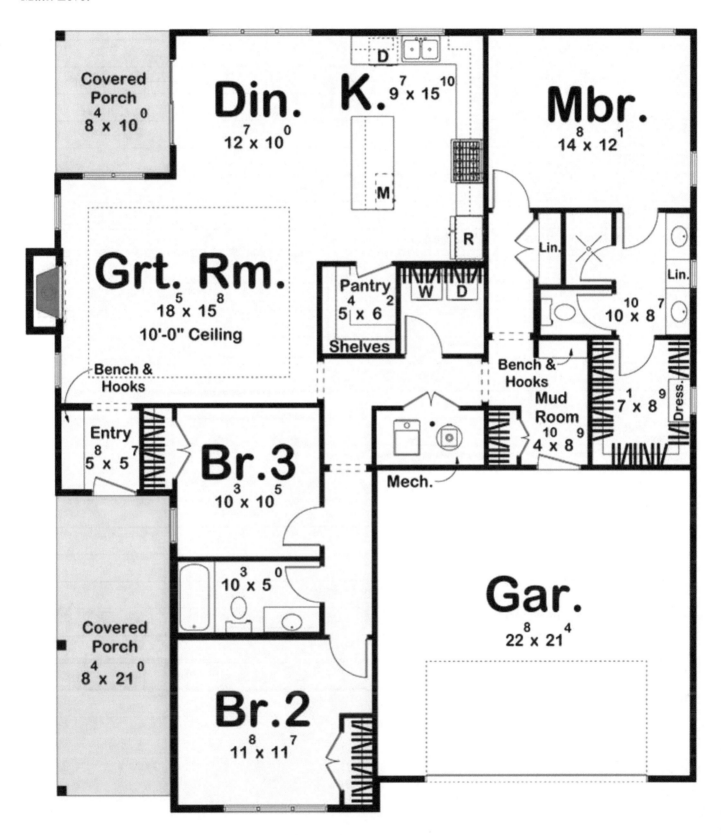

Plan details

Square Footage Breakdown
Total Heated Area:1,658 sq. ft.
1st Floor:1,658 sq. ft.
Porch, Combined:258 sq. ft.
Beds/Baths
Bedrooms:3
Full Bathrooms:2
Foundation Type
Standard Foundations:Slab
Optional Foundations:Walkout, Crawl, Basement
Exterior Walls
Standard Type(s):2x4
Optional Type(s):2x6
Dimensions
Width:48' 0"
Depth:54' 4"
Max Ridge Height:22' 7"
Garage
Type:Attached
Area:498 sq. ft.
Count:2 cars
Entry Location:Front
Ceiling Heights
Floor / Height:First Floor / 9' 0"
Roof Details
Primary Pitch:6 on 12
Secondary Pitch:12 on 12

Stylish and Spacious: Modern 4-Bedroom House Plan for a Rear Sloping Lot

Discover the perfect blend of style and functionality with this modern 4-bedroom house plan, designed specifically for a rear sloping lot. With 4 bedrooms, 2.5 bathrooms, and a generous 3,138 square feet of heated living area, this home offers ample space for comfortable living. Additionally, a 2-car garage provides 464 square feet of parking and convenient access to the home through the foyer. A den located off the foyer offers an ideal work-from-home space, ensuring versatility for your needs.

The heart of this home lies in the well-appointed kitchen, complete with a large island and a tall pantry. The kitchen seamlessly opens to both the dining room and the living room, creating a cohesive and spacious living area. Both the dining room and the living room have access to the back covered balcony, allowing for easy indoor-outdoor flow and providing a delightful space for relaxation and entertainment.

The master suite is a true retreat, occupying the entire right side of the home. With outdoor access, the master suite offers a seamless connection to nature, providing a serene and private space to unwind. Meanwhile, the remaining three bedrooms are located in the finished lower level, ensuring privacy and comfort for family members or guests.

Enjoy a movie night in your own home theater, creating a cinematic experience in the comfort of your own home. Afterward, you can relax and socialize in the inviting rec room or step outside and savor the fresh air on your covered patio, perfect for outdoor gatherings or moments of tranquility.

Experience the perfect combination of style and functionality with this modern 4-bedroom house plan designed for a rear sloping lot. From the spacious kitchen and inviting living areas to the private master suite and versatile lower level, every aspect of this home has been thoughtfully designed to enhance your lifestyle. Customize this plan to fit your unique preferences and create a space that reflects your personal taste. Embrace the contemporary elegance and enjoy the abundance of living space while taking advantage of the seamless indoor-outdoor connection and the peaceful surroundings of your rear sloping lot.

FRONT ELEVATION

REAR ELEVATION

Floor Plan

Main Level

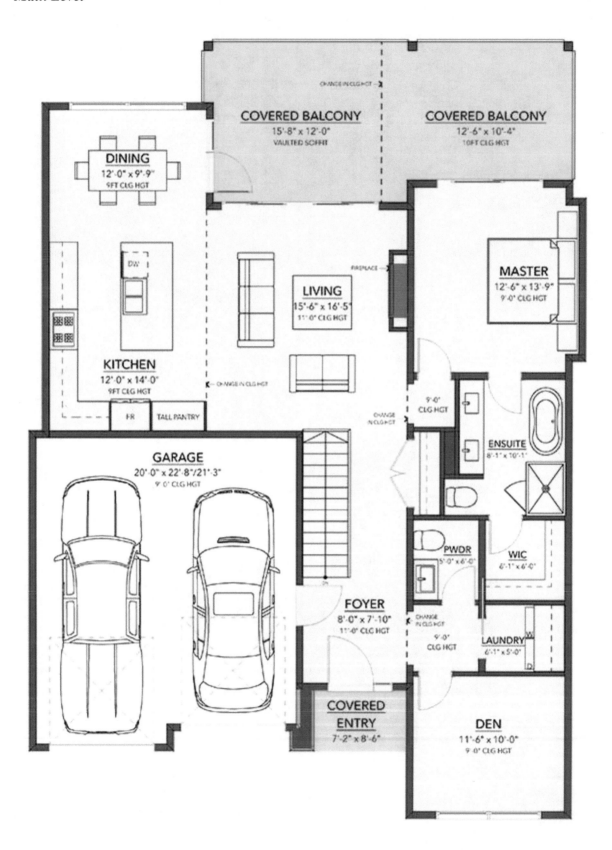

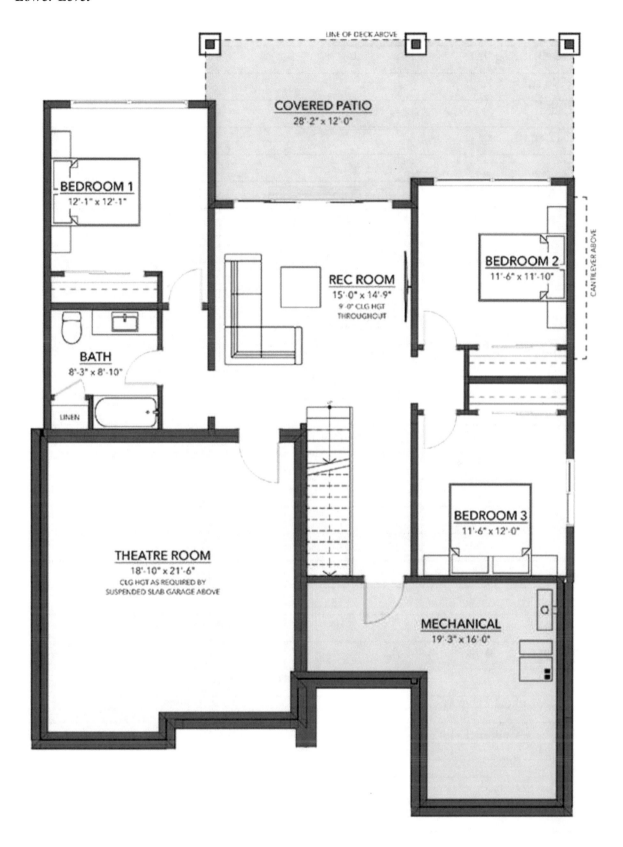

LINE OF DECK ABOVE

COVERED PATIO
28'-2" x 12'-0"

BEDROOM 1
12'-1" x 12'-1"

REC ROOM
15'-0" x 14'-9"
9'-0" CLG HGT
THROUGHOUT

BEDROOM 2
11'-6" x 11'-10"

CANTILEVER ABOVE

BATH
8'-3" x 8'-10"

LINEN

BEDROOM 3
11'-6" x 12'-0"

THEATRE ROOM
18'-10" x 21'-6"
CLG HGT AS REQUIRED BY
SUSPENDED SLAB GARAGE ABOVE

MECHANICAL
19'-3" x 16'-0"

Plan details

Square Footage Breakdown
Total Heated Area:3,138 sq. ft.
Lower Level:1,796 sq. ft.
1st Floor:1,342 sq. ft.
Covered Patio:312 sq. ft.
Deck:312 sq. ft.
Porch, Front:62 sq. ft.

Beds/Baths
Bedrooms:4
Full Bathrooms:2
Half Bathrooms:1

Foundation Type
Standard Foundations:Walkout

Exterior Walls
Standard Type(s):2x6

Dimensions
Width:41' 6"
Depth:58' 0"
Max Ridge Height:19' 3"

Garage
Type:Attached
Area:464 sq. ft.
Count:2 cars
Entry Location:Front

Ceiling Heights
Floor / Height:Lower Level / 9' 0"First Floor / 9' 0"

Room Details	Ceiling Type	Width	Depth	Height
Foyer	Raised	8' 0"	7' 10"	11' 0"
Living Room	Raised	15' 6"	16' 5"	11' 0"
Den		11' 6"	10' 0"	9' 0"

Roof Details
Primary Pitch:3 on 12
Secondary Pitch:1/4 on 12

Made in the USA
Columbia, SC
16 July 2024